50
Scariest Places
and Strangest Mysteries

50
Scariest Places
and Strangest Mysteries

Written by Q. L. Pearce and Phyllis Emert
Illustrations by Brian W. Dow and Lauren Jarrett

BARNES
&NOBLE
BOOKS
NEW YORK

ISBN: 0760703973

Manufactured in the United States of America

10 9 8 7 6 5 4 3 2 1

For Twyla Wardell

SPECIAL THANKS to the following for their help and cooperation in writing this book: Dale Kaczmarek, President of Ghost Research Society (P.O. Box 205, Oak Lawn, Il 60454-0205); Waymon Beinfield of the Alabama Department of Transportation; Department of Parks and Recreation—City and County of Denver; Niagara Frontier State Park and Recreation Commission; George Burgess, Director of the International Shark Attack File—American Elasmobranch Society; and last but not least, my talented editor, Michael "Pappy" Artenstein.

—P. E.

Contents

Journey into the Extraordinary

Do you like a good mystery? Do you like the sensation of chills running up and down your spine? Then you've come to the right place. Our world is filled with tales of strange and scary places, unusual people, lost treasures, and fascinating puzzles. In the following pages, you will find enticing accounts of 50 of the world's most mysterious people and places.

Were ancient advanced civilizations once wiped from the face of the earth in terrible cataclysms? Do strange, primitive creatures thrive in some of the world's deep, cold lakes? How are some people able to walk barefoot across scaling hot coals without the slightest injury to their feet? Do restless, angry spirits roam the halls of Glamis Castle in Scotland?

The purpose of this book is not to make you believe or disbelieve, but to introduce you to the mysteries and scares that have baffled humankind over the centuries. It's fascinating, fast-paced, and frightening. The degrees of mystery and fright range from curiosity and intrigue to creepy uneasiness to heart-stopping terror!

Read, and then decide for yourself whether the fantastic can, in fact, be true. But, one word of warning: Be wary of reading this book when you're alone . . . especially at night.

Into the Fog

When Dr. and Mrs. Gerardo Vidal left a family reunion in Chascomús, Argentina, on June 3, 1968, they expected to make the eighty-mile drive back to their home in Maipù within two hours. They didn't make it. The next time the Vidals were seen in Argentina was when the dazed couple disembarked from a plane that had just arrived from Mexico City—two days later.

The trip had started routinely. The Vidals' neighbors had also attended the party and were driving home by the same route. They later told investigators that they had returned home and waited up to be certain the Vidals arrived safely. After several hours, the neighbors became so worried that they got into their car and drove back, but they saw no sign of the doctor's car along the road. They called local hospitals, but no accidents had been reported.

MEXICO CITY, MEXICO

MAIPÙ, ARGENTINA

Two days went by without a sign of the couple, and then Dr. Vidal called his family from Mexico City to say he and his wife were all right but would need someone to pick them up at the airport in Argentina. When the Vidals arrived, the doctor told his relieved but bewildered family a very strange story.

It seems that during the trip home from the party, they had encountered a dense bank of fog. The doctor could barely see a few inches ahead, when all at once they drove out of the fog bank onto an unfamiliar road. They were astounded to find that although they had been driving late at night, it was suddenly a bright, sunny day. Stunned, Dr. Vidal pulled over and flagged down a passing car. The motorist informed him that they were just outside Mexico City, Mexico (5,000 miles from the Vidals' home), and that 48 hours had passed since they had left the party!

Dr. Vidal reported the incident to the authorities, but no one could say how the couple was suddenly transported from one continent to another! It was noted, however, that the paint had somehow been burned off the entire outside surface of the Vidals' car, a Peugot 403. The damaged car was sent to the United States for examination, and the Vidals were given a new one. But they were never told which agency had provided the new car and taken the old one. The vehicle was never seen again, and to this day, no official explanation has been offered for the bizarre incident.

> ## Missing in Action
> During World War I, British and Turkish troops fiercely battled each other at Gallipoli, a Turkish peninsula. Hill 60 was held by the Turks, and at noon on August 21, 1915, 3,000 Allied troops prepared to attack them. Five hundred soldiers of the British Norfolk Regiment advanced toward the hill. A division of New Zealanders watched in astonishment as the British soldiers entered a thick fog that blanketed the hillside but never marched out. Moments later, the fog reportedly lifted and drifted away, *against* the wind.

The mysterious fog bank that engulfed Dr. and Mrs. Gerardo Vidal sent the Argentinian couple on a journey they would never forget.

The Man in the Velvet Mask

In 1703, a 60-year-old man died after spending 34 years in French prisons. He was perhaps the most famous prisoner in the country's history, but to this day, no one knows his real name. Because of the dark

PARIS, FRANCE

velvet mask that completely covered his face, he is remembered simply as the man in the velvet mask. During his time in prison, he was treated well. He was given fine food, elegant clothing, books, and anything else he desired. But he was kept in isolation. Except to ask for his daily needs, the mysterious prisoner was forbidden to speak. Two guards were always close by the prisoner with orders to kill him immediately if he ever tried to tell his story or remove the mask.

Who was this unnamed prisoner? What had he done to spend his life with his face hidden from the world? After being arrested in Dunkirk in 1669, he was imprisoned by order of the French monarch, Louis XIV, and put under the watchful care of M. Saint-Mars at the prison of Pignerol. In 1698, Saint-Mars became the governor of the prison known as the Bastille, and his secret captive was transferred with him. The mask meant he must have been someone who would easily be recognized, but no important political person was missing during that time. One theory is that he looked extraordinarily like the king himself, prompting many to speculate that the masked man was either the king's father or twin brother.

Whoever he was, he was buried in the parish cemetery of Saint Paul with the mask still in place. Someone made very sure that the identity of the man in the velvet mask would forever remain a secret.

Who was the notorious French prisoner forced to hide his face from the world?

The Footprints of Devon

On the wintry night of February 7, 1855, something roamed unseen in Devonshire, England. The next morning, residents at first were perplexed by the long trail of thousands of footprints in the snow, but

DEVONSHIRE, ENGLAND

they soon became frightened. The strange single-file U-shaped prints were about four inches long and two and a quarter inches wide. They appeared to have been made by a hoofed creature that walked on two legs. In some places the prints suggested that the thing had cloven (split) hooves, and it was soon nicknamed the Devil of Devon.

Even animal experts were bewildered by the bizarre tracks in the snow. The prints were very regular, about 8 inches apart, and continued in a zigzag pattern for 97 miles. The trail led from house to house as if the creature had purposefully gone to each door, then crept away. Whatever made the prints had leapt over walls and onto rooftops without changing the stride length of 8 inches. At the banks of the frozen Exe River where the wide, shallow waterway met the sea, the footprints ended, then started up again on the other side, two miles away.

In some places, there were gaps in the trail. The prints might suddenly appear in a garden and then end just as suddenly in a snowy field. In another area, the trail of prints entered a shed and exited through a six-inch-wide hole in the wall on the other side. The next day, hundreds of people saw the mysterious footprints. It seemed that everyone had an

Though long since melted away, the eerie footprints that appeared in the snow one morning in Devonshire, England, remain frozen in time as one of the strangest mysteries on record.

opinion about what made them. Many animals were suggested, including a fox, badger, rabbit, donkey, even a kangaroo. One by one, the choices were eliminated. What animal could travel nearly 100 miles in a single night, in such a straight line, and over, under, or through so many obstructions?

Some people insisted that the footprints were made by the devil. They locked their doors, shuttered their windows, and refused to leave their homes after sunset. As additional proof, they pointed out that when the prints led into some dense undergrowth, tracking dogs howled in panic and refused to follow any farther. What else, the people reasoned, could possibly terrify the dogs so? Whatever it was, the footprints of Devon melted away with the snow and were never seen again.

The Anasazi

Imagine yourself in the hot, dry desert of the American Southwest, far from the nearest city or town. From somewhere close by, you hear the warning buzz of a rattlesnake. A startled jackrabbit sprints across your path, raising clouds of rust-colored dust. The only shade is beneath the overhang of a towering sandstone cliff. But relief from the blazing sun is not all you find among the shadows. Tucked under the massive rock are the remains of a great civilization, the ancient dwellings of the remarkable Anasazi Indians.

The name *Anasazi* is Navajo for "the old ones." We know that the Anasazi settled the Southwest about the time the Roman Empire was at its peak in Europe, but the exact origin and fate of this unique civilization is still a mystery. Their abandoned cities have been described as some of the greatest architectural achievements of the Southwest. One of the finest examples of their work is Chaco Canyon in northwestern New Mexico, an extraordinary settlement 9 miles long and once capable of housing 5,000 people.

CHACO CANYON,
NEW MEXICO

Pueblo Bonito, or "beautiful village," the largest building in Chaco Canyon, was five stories high. It was made of bricks carved from the sun-baked soil, its plastered walls decorated with colorful paintings.

Excellent farmers, the Anasazi built huge water reservoirs that fed into miles of irrigation channels, enabling them to grow crops such as corn, squash, and beans even in their hot, dry environment. They also grew cotton, which they wove into fine fabrics. Their skills were not limited to cloth, though. Anasazi baskets were so tightly woven that they could be used for carrying water!

Credited with some of the greatest architectural achievements of the American Southwest, the Anasazi nevertheless abandoned their brilliant cities in hasty fashion.

Deserted Roads

Anasazi villages were connected by nearly 400 miles of roads that were 30 feet wide and almost perfectly straight. When faced with an obstacle on the road, such as a cliff wall, the builders actually cut stairs into the stone, keeping the road on a straight path. Why would they go to so much trouble when they could have simply gone around the barriers? Another mystery is why the roads were needed at all. The Anasazi had neither horses nor the wheel, and traveling on foot didn't require such elaborate avenues. Why did they spend years carving the roads into the desolate desert?

Around the year 1300, the Anasazi deserted the marvelous cities they had built, leaving them to tumble into ruin. Some people left personal belongings behind as if they expected to return for them. But instead, the Anasazis virtually vanished into the desert. Researchers are not certain why the Indians left their homes so suddenly. One theory is that a drought made the land useless for growing crops. Recently a burial site has been uncovered that includes the remains of several hundred Anasazi. The bones show some evidence of violence. Also, it appears that all of the windows on the lowest level of Pueblo Bonito were closed up. Was it done for defensive reasons? Were the Anasazi victims of a brutal enemy? Perhaps the secret of their fate is locked somewhere in the crumbling stones.

The Ghost Dogs of Ballechin House

Major Stewart of Perthshire, Scotland, loved his beautiful country mansion, Ballechin House. He lived there happily for more than 40 years with his many beloved dogs. Stewart cared deeply for the animals, and the mansion was as much their home as it was his. When he died in 1876, he left behind 14 canine companions. His final wish was that they should be properly provided for. But the major's nephew, who inherited Ballechin House, didn't share his uncle's deep feelings for the animals, and the dogs were put to sleep.

Soon after, the nephew's wife was in the study reading when she plainly smelled the odor of a dog. Then, to her astonishment, she felt an unseen animal cautiously nuzzle her hand. The odd events happened again and again, and although the phantoms seemed harmless, the family finally moved and rented the home to others. It wasn't long before the new tenants reported being nuzzled and nudged by the spectral dogs. They also heard strange whimpering and scratching sounds at night.

Eventually a representative of the Psychical Research Society rented Ballechin House for a single evening and invited 35 guests in the hopes of experiencing some contact with the spirit world. They were not disappointed. The gathering had barely begun when guests heard inexplicable noises, including footsteps, scratching, whining, and other odd sounds. Several people accused the host of trickery and demanded that everyone assemble in one room—the library. It was then that there came an unusual pounding on the

door of the library. One after another, the guests claimed to see the hazy figure of a spaniel dog. Were the startled guests victims of some sort of illusion? Maybe the rightful residents of Ballechin House were simply unwilling to leave their cherished home.

In Ballechin House, the dogs are loyal to their master in life—and beyond!

The Monster of Lake Champlain

On July 5, 1977, a woman by the name of Sandra Mansi took a most unusual snapshot. She reportedly saw a commotion in the otherwise peaceful waters of Lake Champlain, a huge body of water that stretches along the northern border between the states of New York and Vermont. It began with a rippling that Mansi first thought to be caused by a school of fish. Then, to her surprise, something began to rise from the water. It was the head and long, slender neck of some sort of animal. Stunned, the woman managed to focus and shoot the snapshot before the creature disappeared.

Mansi didn't report the incident immediately, fearing that people might think she was crazy. But eventually, since others also had claimed to see the extraordinary animal, she informed the authorities and turned over the photograph for close scrutiny. The experts who inspected the picture seemed to feel that it was authentic, but no one could identify the creature. Since

Before Sandra Mansi's photograph of Champ was lost, experts who had seen the picture had considered it to be authentic.

that time, the original photo and the negative have been lost.

The first written record of the beast, who is known as Champ, was made in 1609 by the man the lake was named for, French explorer Samuel

LAKE CHAMPLAIN

de Champlain. He described it as a 20-foot-long snakelike creature with a horse-shaped head. In August of 1878, six people on a pleasure cruise of the lake sighted Champ, or one of its descendants, again. The witnesses claimed they had seen a beast about 50 feet long, with a long neck and two folds at the back of its head, swimming smoothly through the water. They also added that it appeared to have three humps on its back. Since then there have been dozens of similar reports.

Is there an undiscovered life-form in the cold, deep body of water? Lake Champlain is 100 miles long and 13 miles across at its widest point. Its deepest point measures some 400 feet. Certainly something might inhabit this humongous lake and manage to remain hidden, despite exhaustive search efforts. In the 1800s, circus showman P. T. Barnum offered a $50,000 reward to anyone who could provide positive proof of the creature's existence. The reward was never collected.

LAKE MONSTERS OF THE WORLD

Champ isn't the only frightful monster reportedly seen in the world's deep, cold lakes. Here is a list of a few of the others:

MONSTER	LOCATION
Manipogo	Lake Manitoba, Canada
Ogopogo	Okanagan Lake, British Columbia, Canada
Silver Lake Monster	Silver Lake, New York
Slimey Slim	Lake Payette, Idaho
Gloucester Monster	Gloucester Harbor, Massachusetts
Flathead Lake Monster	Flathead Lake, Montana
Morag	Loch Morar, Scotland
Loch Ness Monster	Loch Ness, Scotland
The Great Lake Monster	Storsjon, Sweden

The Lost Continent of Mu

The Pacific Ocean is the world's largest body of water. It covers millions of square miles, and ships can sail for weeks without sighting land. But was this always so? Many Polynesian legends tell of a vanished land in the Pacific Ocean—a place of magnificent cities and a great civilization.

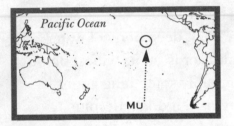

In their 2,000-year-old stories of creation, the Hopi Indians of North America describe an enormous region west of their land where a technically advanced society waged war in flying vehicles. These tales have something else unusual in common. In each of these accounts, the land, which has come to be called the continent of Mu, was destroyed in a series of horrendous earthquakes and floods.

Did a huge land mass once exist in the Pacific Ocean? In 1926, Colonel James Churchward wrote a book called *The Lost Continent of Mu.* The author claimed to have based the information in it on two sets of tablets called the Naacal tablets. Churchward reported that one set of the tablets was from India and the other set had been discovered thousands of miles away in Mexico. The tablets were said to be about 12,000 years old and inscribed with a mystical language, called Naacal, which Churchward believed was spoken in the land of Mu. (The colonel claimed to have been taught the language by a Hindu priest in India.)

According to Churchward, Mu straddled the equator and stretched some 5,000 miles long and 3,000 miles wide. It neared the shores of the Hawaiian Islands in the west and Rapa Nui in the East. He wrote that as

Sunk!

How could a whole continent be submerged? Churchward proposed that a huge belt of gas existed in caverns in the earth's crust beneath Mu. He suggested that about 12,000 years ago the caverns collapsed and Mu sank. Recently some scientists have discovered evidence that such gas belts may exist in porous rock deep within the earth.

far back as 50,000 years ago, the people of Mu had developed a highly advanced civilization that flourished until about 12,000 years ago. At one time Mu supposedly had a population of more than 60 million people!

If Mu really did exist, its end probably didn't come all at once. According to Churchward, the southern part of the continent was devastated first by earthquakes. The terrified survivors fled north, but they could not escape their doom. About 200 years later, Mu sank in a tremendous upheaval.

Did a highly advanced race of people exist well before the great civilization of Egypt? Is it possible that an entire continent disappeared beneath the surface of the Pacific?

Are the Naacal tablets the only remaining link to a civilization that once existed in what is now the Pacific Ocean?

The Flying Dutchman

Three quarters of the earth is covered by water. The great oceans are the keepers of mysteries and the spawning grounds of myths—stories of sea monsters, mermaids, and the like. Perhaps the most horrifying is the tale of the *Flying Dutchman.*

According to the legend, a 17th-century Dutch sea captain, Cornelius Vanderdecken, was known for taking extreme risks even in stormy seas.

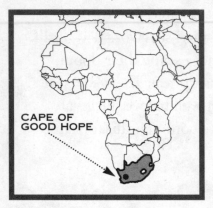

CAPE OF GOOD HOPE

On a disastrous trip around the Cape of Good Hope at the southern tip of Africa, during a fierce storm, he chose a short but dangerous route close to the rocky shore. When one terrified sailor begged him to change his mind, the captain threw the unfortunate man overboard. Vanderdecken then defiantly shook his fist at the heavens and swore that he would sail his ship until Judgment Day, if necessary. Suddenly, a glowing figure appeared on the deck and declared that Vanderdecken had chosen his own fate. The ship was condemned to sail forever without reaching port. To this day, some sailors believe that the ship, which has come to be known as the *Flying Dutchman,* still sails, and that its sighting is a warning of impending doom.

Is this just one more fanciful tale of the sea? Strangely, sightings of the arrogant sea captain and his cursed vessel have been reported for 300 years. It is probably accurate to chalk up most of the sightings to a trick of light or perhaps an overly tired sailor with an active imagination, but some reports are not so easily dismissed. In 1881, one frightening account was sworn to by 13 sailors (including the captain) of the HMS *Bacchante.*

Condemned to sail the ocean forever, Dutch sea captain Cornelius Vanderdecken and his cursed vessel are a sign of impending doom to any unsuspecting seafarer.

The night was clear and the sea was calm. In the log, the captain of the *Bacchante* described the ghost ship as passing silently across the bow, bathed in an eerie red glow. The ancient masts and rigging were unmistakable. One of the witnesses, a young midshipman, is considered a particularly reliable source. He would eventually be known as George V, the king of England.

True to the legend, on the day of the sighting, the man who had first seen the *Flying Dutchman* was killed in a fall from the fore topmast. Tragedy also awaited the captain of the *Bacchante*. When he finally reached port, he felt the need to see a doctor and was given the news that he was dying of a fatal illness.

The phantom ship evidently has been seen many times since, but one sighting was especially interesting because it included a phantom storm. In 1911, the whaling ship *Orkney Belle* was off the coast of Iceland in fairly calm seas when the crew reportedly witnessed the *Flying Dutchman* battling a nonexistent storm. The ghost ship rose and fell in the waves, and its sails strained in the wind as it raced by the *Orkney Belle*, but the terrified sailors felt no signs of a real storm. Fortunately, unlike the crew of the *Bacchante*, none of the whaler's crew suffered any harm.

The Bermuda Triangle

"We cannot see land. . . . Everything is wrong . . . strange. We can't be sure of our position. We seem to be lost. Even the sea doesn't look as it should."

That was part of the last message the control tower received from five Navy planes with fourteen crew members aboard on December 5, 1945. Flight 19 had left Fort Lauderdale, Florida, that afternoon for a training

mission. When all contact was lost, a rescue plane was sent out immediately, but that plane vanished as well. No wreckage was ever discovered.

These planes, and more than 100 other ships and planes carrying a total of about 1000 people, have been inexplicably lost in a huge patch of ocean known as the Bermuda Triangle. As with Flight 19, sometimes there is contact before the disappearance, and the victims report that their equipment has failed, or that the ocean looks "different."

Often no sign of the ship or plane is discovered, but that isn't always the case. In 1940, the French ship *Rosalie* was found adrift with only a cat, fowl, and canary aboard. Her cargo was safe and there was little weather damage. What happened to her human crew? In 1944, the Cuban ship *Rubicon* was discovered undamaged with only a dog onboard, but the crew had simply vanished. And in 1969, a ship called the *Vagabond* was discovered under way but deserted.

The odd occurrences are not limited to disappearances. One pilot, his plane battered by turbulence on a flight to Jacksonville, Florida, sent out a Mayday but received no reply. Fifteen minutes later, he managed to land at Jacksonville at approximately the same time that the tower was receiving his distress call!

In June of 1986, an experienced crew flying a large PBY-6A Catalina from Bermuda to Florida reportedly flew into a thick yellow cloud that they described as being something like "eggnog." Some of the plane's gauges began to spin, and others provided ridiculous readings. Because the radio went dead and the cloud had completely cut off visibility, the crew had to fly blind for several hours. Then, just as suddenly as it appeared, the cloud disappeared, and the instruments returned to normal. Since then, other pilots have reported flying into mysterious, sometimes glowing clouds that render their instruments useless.

What forces are at work in the Bermuda Triangle? Besides the high rate of unexplained events, scientists have found nothing about the area to set it apart from any other. Some people blame the problems on space aliens or sea monsters. Others think sudden storms, waterspouts, freak waves, currents, or tides are responsible.

Perhaps someday we will learn the truth, but until then, the Bermuda Triangle remains one of the most feared ocean areas in the world.

The five Navy planes that disappeared on December 5, 1945, set the stage for more than 100 subsequent disappearances in the Bermuda Triangle.

31

El Dorado

More than 400 years ago, on the shores of a clear, cold lake on the Cundinamarca Plateau in what is now Colombia, Indians gathered for an astonishing ceremony. A tall, proud-looking man stood at the edge of the water, his entire body smeared with a sticky substance. Attendants blew gleaming handfuls of gold dust at him until he glistened in the morning sun and so became El Dorado, "the gilded one." The man, a tribal chieftain, then stepped onto the center of an elaborate balsa raft. The oarsmen, with their backs turned toward him, rowed to the deepest part of the lake, and there the chieftain leapt into the icy water. The gold dust swirled slowly into the sunlit water and rained down to the depths as an offering to either the god of the sun or a goddess of the lake. Priests, too, threw offerings of golden trinkets and glittering emeralds. According to a legend of the Chibcha Indians of Colombia, this ceremony was performed year after year by a tribe to the north of their land, and every year the treasure at the bottom of the lake grew. But was it just a legend?

CUNDINAMARCA, COLOMBIA

In 1513, the Chibcha Indians told Spanish conquistadores about the Indians to their north who performed the ceremony of El Dorado. According to their stories, these mysterious Indians practically covered their city with thin sheets of gold, and also used the precious metal to fashion elegant jewelry and ornaments. To the greedy Spaniards, El Dorado the man became Eldorado the place—a city of gold. By the 1530s, many adventurers had set out to find the fabled city, but they met with failure and often with death in the region's rugged mountains and dense jungles.

In 1536, Gonzalo Jimenez de Quesada left Santa Marta, Colombia, with 900 men to search for Eldorado. The terrain the Spaniards encountered when crossing the Andes was extremely difficult and dangerous, and hundreds of soldiers died. By the time Quesada came across the Chibcha Indians, his force had already dwindled to 200. The Chibchas displayed some gold and emeralds but told the Spaniards to continue northward to a place called Lake Guatavita, where the ceremony of El Dorado supposedly took place. Quesada and his men finally found the lake but no riches. They returned home empty-handed and disappointed.

Over the centuries, attempts were made to drain Lake Guatavita for treasure. Some gold and emeralds were found in the mud of the exposed banks, but the task was daunting. As time passed, the legend of El Dorado gradually loosened its grip on fortune hunters. Then, in 1969, two farmers found a small but remarkable Indian sculpture in a cave near Bogotá, Colombia. The sculpture brought El Dorado out of the realm of fable and into the realm of possibility. It was a golden model of a raft powered by eight oarsmen with their backs to an elaborately decorated central figure. Was the statue made to commemorate an event that actually happened?

In 1969, a small but remarkable Indian sculpture was found in a cave near Bogotá, Colombia. The sculpture depicts the much-fabled ceremony of El Dorado.

Firewalkers

Imagine that you are on the island of Fiji in the South Pacific, standing near a sand pit about four feet deep and twenty feet long. You watch as islanders fill the pit with wood and smooth, flat stones. Next, the wood is set aflame and allowed to burn until the red-hot stones rest on a bed of coals. The fire is so hot that you have to move well away from the edge of the pit to avoid being scorched. A barefoot priest in traditional garb, called a *mbete* (mm-BET-ay), and his dutiful followers then step onto the sizzling stones without hesitation. Slowly and deliberately, they walk the full length of the pit.

This scene is not imaginary; it actually takes place on the Fiji Islands in full view of dozens of spectators. After prayer and intense concentration to bring the believers to an almost hypnotic state, the priest leads the firewalkers across the fiery pit.

The firewalkers are not prepared physically with any special oils or protective chemicals. Their feet have thick soles, but they do respond to being pricked by a pin, so they can certainly feel pain. Nevertheless, if mentally prepared, they are never burned or blistered. In fact, the skin of their feet rarely even becomes warm during the ceremony, and there is seldom damage to their body hair or clothing. Scientists are baffled and have yet to come up with a satisfactory explanation for this astonishing feat.

Pacific Ocean

FIJI ISLANDS

Although the origin of the custom and when and where it first developed is unknown, today, firewalking is practiced in Sri Lanka and India as well as parts of the Middle East and Australia (there are even references to it in classical Greek and ancient Chinese documents). Observers there, too, report that participants walk barefoot with no preparation across

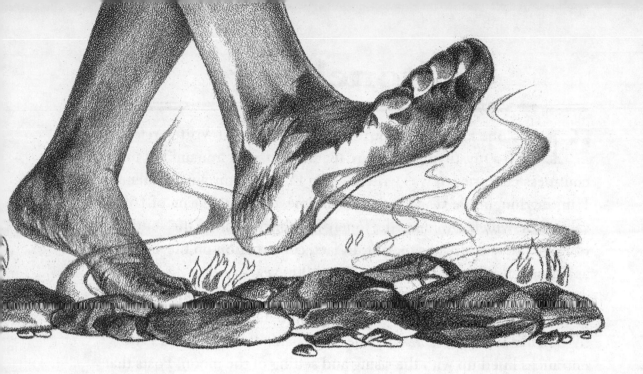

*For centuries, some have had the ability to walk
over red-hot coals without burning their feet—
a phenomenon still unexplainable today.*

stones or coals heated to temperatures of more than 900 degrees
Fahrenheit. Firewalkers in Hawaii have even successfully strolled across
still-smoking pools of lava!

The firewalking ceremonies are performed for many reasons, including to prove one's faith, to prove a person's innocence if he or she is
accused of a crime, or simply to purify the soul. In some places, it is even
performed to insure a good harvest.

Some nonislanders have been badly burned or blistered trying this,
but others have been successful. They claim they can feel the heat, but that
it is not painful. They also claim to feel a tingling sensation that has been
described as what happens when your foot falls asleep—almost like tiny
electrical shocks on their soles.

Stonehenge

"No one knows what or why." That is the first written reference to a mystifying structure that has puzzled humankind for countless centuries. It was written by an English churchman, Henry of Huntingdon, in the year 1130. At that time, the double ring of 162 colossal stones, which dominate the lonely Salisbury Plain in the southern part of England, was already ancient. In fact, construction on the site, known as Stonehenge, probably began some 4,000 years ago!

Stonehenge was built in three main stages. First, around 2800 B.C., primitive Neolithic (New Stone Age) people dug a large circular ditch with high banks known as a *henge.* The inner bank of the ditch had two entrances lined up with the rising and setting of the moon. Posts that helped to chart the moon's movements once stood at the northeast end of

the henge, along with a huge rectangular stone known as the Heel Stone, which might have marked the rising of the sun at a particular time each year. Around the outside were more than 50 unusual pits, called the Aubrey Holes. Some contained burned human remains. Was the early Stonehenge a place for both sacrifice and burial? Was it perhaps dedicated to some long-forgotten deity of the moon?

SALISBURY, ENGLAND

Around 2200 B.C., a group called the Beaker People, named for the drinking cups found in their graves, added eighty huge rectangular blue-stones (they actually have a bluish tint), weighing about seven tons each, in two concentric circles. The bluestone originated from mountains in Wales 240 miles away! Whether it was brought to the site on purpose or simply left there by ancient glaciers is unknown. The Beaker People then filled in the ditch in a particular place so that a small area lined up with the sunrise at summer solstice (the longest day of the year).

In the final stages of building, which began around 2000 B.C., the bluestones were rearranged and a circle of huge sandstone blocks, called sarsen stones, was added. The upright stones are about 13 feet tall and topped with massive slabs of rock. Within is a horseshoe of sandstone, then a smaller horseshoe of bluestones.

Why was Stonehenge built? Was it constructed as an ancient observatory? Or as a temple for practicing mystic religious rites? Few researchers think it was strictly an astronomical observatory, but it may have been used to keep track of the seasons. Many people think Stonehenge was primarily a sacred place used by priests. By 1000 B.C., however, the site was deserted. Now Stonehenge stands alone. Perhaps the answers to the many questions it poses still lie buried on that bleak, windy plain.

Was Stonehenge once the site of human sacrifice and burial?

37

Ancient Maps

Some people claim that when Christopher Columbus sailed on his fateful journey to the Americas in 1492, he carried maps that already showed the approximate position of the western continents. Although the maps have never been found, it is believed that they were based on maps

ANTARCTICA

that had been drawn nearly 2,000 years earlier. Is it possible that such knowledge existed at that time? If so, who gathered the information that Columbus's maps were based upon?

In 1513, 21 years after Columbus's journey, a map was drawn by a Turkish naval officer named Piri Ibn Haji Memmed, also known as Piri Re'is. He claimed to have based his work on the maps that had been carried by Columbus. Although not perfect, the map detailed South America's interior and western coast, which had not yet been explored by Europeans. The map also showed the coastline of Antarctica as it would appear without ice. But the continent of Antarctica was not officially sighted until 1820!

Why are these maps so surprising? The continent of Antarctica is almost entirely covered by an ice sheet that is in some places two miles thick. The Piri Re'is and other maps indicate that the ancient mapmakers not only knew about the frozen continent, but they seem to have known what the land was like under the ice. Such information would have to have been gathered before the ice sheet was as massive as it is now. But the Antarctic ice sheet has existed since well *before* humans have been mapping the globe.

The Oronteus Finaeus map, copied in 1532 from a mysterious old map, is even more detailed than the Piri Re'is map. It shows the paths of ancient rivers on Antarctica. Modern glaciers appear to follow those same paths. Like rivers, glaciers move or "flow" downhill in the easiest route, so if ancient riverbeds actually exist under the ice, the glaciers would probably follow them.

The Buache map of 1754 is also quite remarkable. On it, Antarctica is drawn as two islands, one much larger than the other, with a narrow channel between. It wasn't until 1955, during the Geophysical Year expeditions, that the underlying structure of Antarctica began to be revealed, including riverbeds, mountains, and the general shape of the land, which appeared to be made up of two parts. Now, satellite imaging has shown the size and shape of the continent, and that it is indeed made up of two parts.

Who were the ancient mapmakers? Did visitors actually set foot on the continent of Antarctica many centuries ago at a time before the ice had claimed all the land? If so, were they representatives of an ancient civilization that has since disappeared from the face of the earth?

Did visitors actually set foot on the continent of Antarctica many centuries before the ice claimed all the land? Some ancient maps seem to indicate as much.

Nan Madol

The first outsider known to visit Nan Madol was a shipwrecked sailor named James O'Connell in 1828. He was treated kindly by the natives of Pohnpei, the largest island in the Caroline Archipelago of Micronesia, northeast of New Guinea. He was even allowed to visit the strange abandoned ruins offshore, a smaller piece of land known as Nan Madol. But the native who took him there by canoe was terrified and would not set foot on the place. The people of Pohnpei believed that the ruins were haunted by the spirits of the dead rulers and priests who once lived there and are buried in massive vaults on some of the smaller islands, called islets.

According to one legend, two brothers, Ohlosihpa and Ohlosohpa, arrived in a canoe from the west and built Nan Madol in a single day. They supposedly used magic and made the stones fly into place. When you first see the incredible island-city, which covers some 175 acres, that explanation doesn't seem so farfetched. Immense broken boulders of coral were somehow dredged up from the reef and used as landfill to create more than ninety small islets behind a protective sea wall that sheltered it from the ocean waves. Nan Madol means "the place of spaces," which probably refers to the channels between the islets. On platforms over the coral, a native workforce built palaces, temples, vaults, and tombs with columns of volcanic rock (basalt) quarried miles away on the main island. Some of the naturally formed columns were as long as 25 feet and weighed many tons.

Construction began about A.D. 500 in the quiet lagoon just off Pohnpei and continued over centuries. One of the many mysteries of Nan Madol is why it wasn't built on the main island. It certainly would have been easier to construct such an enclosure near where the basalt was

The enormous island-city of Nan Madol covers some 175 acres and once boasted magnificent palaces, temples, vaults, and tombs.

quarried. Instead, the workers had to endure great difficulties to carry the stone columns by raft, then somehow hoist them as high as 60 feet in the air to reach the building site. It is likely that the inhabitants of the enclosure—the priests and the rulers, called Saudeleurs, and their families—wanted to separate themselves from the rest of the population.

According to oral legends passed down by the mainlanders, the Saudeleurs were thought to be descendants of Ohlosohpa and to possess great magic. They had absolute power and insisted on having the best of everything, leaving little for the rest of the population. Finally, the natives had had enough. Around the year 1600, a warrior named Isokelekel led 333 men in a revolt that ended with the overthrow of the Saudeleurs. The work on Nan Madol stopped forever.

Today, Nan Madol is in ruins. Some of it has been claimed by the ocean, much of it by the lush jungle. Its enormous stone structures have stood empty for nearly four centuries, and if ghosts from the past walk along its stone corridors, they walk alone.

The Olmecs

Over a century ago, the remains of a previously unknown race of Indians were discovered by a Mexican farmer. We have no idea what the Indians called themselves, but they are now known as the Olmecs, or "dwellers in the land of rubber." No matter what they are called, one thing is certain: They were the first advanced civilization to flower in Central America.

Rubber trees were plentiful on the swampy jungle coast along the Gulf of Mexico where the Olmecs settled. It was a hot, humid land with lots of rainfall. The first traces of these remarkably intelligent people date back to around 1200 or 1300 B.C., near what is now Veracruz and Tabasco, in southern Mexico. But there is no clue as to where they came from.

It's likely that the mysterious Olmecs were warriors who practiced human sacrifice. Stone altars have been discovered at some sites, with carved bowls that probably held liquid (blood, perhaps). Cannibalized human bones also have been found nearby. Nevertheless, the Olmecs were surprisingly advanced. They had their own calendar as well as a knowledge of astronomy. It is thought that they developed a system of written numbers that was later used by the Mayans, a group of Indian

Some of the huge stone heads attributed to the Olmecs stand 10 feet high and weigh as much as 30 tons.

42

peoples from Central America and Mexico. There is evidence that they had even designed a compass of sorts using lodestone (a natural magnet).

The largest of the Olmec centers of civilization, La Venta, was built on a small sandy island, two miles square. At its heart was a flattened cone-shaped pyramid more than 100 feet tall, made of 3.5 million cubic feet of clay. The remains of a ball court formed by a small step pyramid, a platform, and two earthen mounds also have been discovered. The ball game appears to have been some kind of cross between soccer and baseball.

VERACRUZ, MEXICO

In some cases, the end of the Olmec civilization was abrupt and mysterious. In the Olmec city of San Lorenzo, the destruction (around 900 B.C.) seems to have been particularly brutal. From the condition and location of artifacts from that period, it seems that artwork was suddenly smashed or mutilated and statues buried, mostly facedown. Were the Olmecs themselves the cause of the destruction? When a ruler died, did they try to erase the evidence of his rule? Other Olmec centers survived longer, but by about 100 B.C., the Olmecs had disappeared. What happened to them? Where did they go? There is still much to learn about this unusual mother culture of Central America.

Olmec art included beautifully carved jewelry, figures, stone slabs, and altars, but the huge stone heads with heavy down-turned lips, staring eyes, and broad, flat noses are truly outstanding. Carved from a single piece of basalt, some are 10 feet high and weigh as much as 30 tons. The blocks of stone were probably rafted downriver from the Tuxtla Mountains 60 miles away. Still, there is no trace of the tools or refuse from the carvings, so the actual carving site is unknown. That is only one of the many puzzles yet to be solved about the Olmec civilization.

Some of the magnificent statues that appear to guard the coast of Easter Island are said to be over 1,000 years old.

Easter Island

On Easter Sunday, 1722, Dutch explorer Jacob Roggeveen came upon the tiny, remote island of Rapa Nui in the South Pacific Ocean, 2,300 miles west of Chile. It has since been known to outsiders as Easter Island. Roggeveen, the first European to visit Rapa Nui, was astonished to see the desolate, wave-swept coast guarded by mysterious statues, each with the same strange features—long ears, squared chins, rounded bellies, and no legs. Some wore an oversized red stone headpiece. Most of the statues were between 12 and 15 feet tall and weighed about 15 to 20 tons. The largest, however,

was an unfinished statue that had never been raised to an upright position. It was nearly 90 feet tall and probably exceeded 100 tons.

Today, most of the statues, called *moai*, have been toppled and offer few clues to the riddle of who carved them and why. It is likely that they once held some religious significance and may represent ancestors of the islanders. Perhaps they were meant to guard the tiny island from the dangers of the sea. Some natives claim the statues had *mana*, or supernatural power.

It seems that the oldest of the *moai* was carved from volcanic stone nearly 1,300 years ago. The craftsmen, who used hatchets and chisels made of black obsidian (volcanic glass), were incredibly skilled and patient (it may have taken as long as a year to carve a single statue). More than 800 *moai* have been discovered, some completed, some not. In fact, many were left half finished, with the carver's tools dropped beside them as if he had deserted his chore quite suddenly.

How these massive statues were put in place on their stone platforms, called *ahus,* is just one of the mysteries surrounding this strange place. Some were moved as far as 10 miles from the volcanic quarry where they were carved. (The quarry still contains some 300 statues in various stages of completion.) Evidence has been found of a system of cords and cables that may have been used to slide and drag the finished statues along, but many natives say that the statues walked into place using their own *mana.*

What meaning did the *moai* truly hold for the natives? The answer to that may be forever lost in the mists of time. The islanders have no written language today, only a few wooden tablets that have been carried down from generation to generation. The tablets are covered with a curious written language of the past. Unfortunately, the meanings behind the writings were not passed on. In the 1800s, many islanders were captured by slave traders from South America and taken far away. Among the captives were the few islanders who might have been able to translate the writing on the tablets. When they died, that knowledge died with them. Now it appears there is no one left to help solve the puzzle of the statues of Easter Island, and the mysterious *moai* simply stare mutely out to sea.

Spring-Heeled Jack

The city of London, England, certainly has had its share of strange stories, from the spirits of the infamous Tower of London to the gruesome tales of Jack the Ripper. One of the oddest, though, is the story of Spring-Heeled Jack.

In 1837, police began to get reports of an incredible figure crossing a local park in tremendous leaps. The sightings had been at night, so observers couldn't give many details, but all agreed that no human was capable of jumping so high and so far. The story was unusual, but it seemed that whatever the thing was, it hadn't harmed anyone. The press ran a few articles and dubbed the mysterious creature Spring-Heeled Jack.

LONDON, ENGLAND

Little was made of it until one night a year later, when Jane Alsop answered a furious hammering at the door of the home she shared with her sister on Bearbind Lane in London. A man stood outside, half hidden in shadow. He identified himself as a police officer and ordered her to bring out a light, for they had caught Spring-Heeled Jack. The girl raced back inside and returned quickly with a candle. As Jane handed it to him, the man suddenly grabbed her by the wrist and pulled her close enough so that she could see his glowing eyes. Horrified, Jane wrenched her arm away, but he seized her long hair and scratched at her face. Drawn by her shrieks, Jane's sister rushed to help her, and the man bounded away toward the street in a few great leaps.

Later, the terrified girl described her attacker as a ghastly man wearing some sort of helmet and a tight white oilskin costume. In tears, she swore that his eyes were like balls of fire and that he had spouted flames

47

Who—or what—was the strange
being who bounded his way into
British legend forever?

and had ripped at her with his long curved claws.

Over the next 30 years, Spring-Heeled Jack was sighted dozens of times. In a few cases, pranksters were caught trying to imitate him. Some very reputable people, however, claimed that they were attacked by him, although he never did any serious harm. A pair of army sentries once reported that he had slipped up behind them and slapped one sentry with an icy cold hand, then leapt onto the roof of the guardhouse in a single bound. People even set traps to capture him, but he would simply laugh as he escaped. Then, for some unknown reason, he seemed to disappear. For a long time there were no sightings at all until, around the turn of the century, reports of Spring-Heeled Jack began to trickle in again.

The last sighting was in 1904, when he was almost caught in Liverpool. A crowd had cornered him, but he leapt from a darkened street to the rooftops and melted into the darkness, never to be seen again.

Were people just getting carried away by the strange story? Was the press encouraging a fantasy in order to sell newspapers? Or did Spring-Heeled Jack really exist?

The Great Pyramid at Giza

The only surviving example of the Seven Wonders of the Ancient World stands like a massive sentry in the desert sands of the Nile Valley—the Great Pyramid at Giza. Now its darkened passages are hauntingly silent, but one can't help but imagine the awesome burial rituals that must have taken place there when the body of the Egyptian pharaoh Cheops was laid to rest.

The Great Pyramid, flanked by two smaller pyramids, was begun some 45 centuries ago. It took about 30 years to build, with a workforce numbering in the hundreds of thousands. Built on the Giza Plateau on the right bank of the Nile about 10 miles from the modern city of Cairo, the pyramid covers 13 acres and is taller than a 40-story building.

Its 2.3 million building stones (enough to build a wall 10 feet high and a foot wide around the entire country of France) weighed from 2.5 to 15 tons each. Amazingly, the four corners of the pyramid are almost perfect right angles, and the sides face the four points of the compass almost exactly. The gleaming white casing stones of limestone that once covered the finished pyramid were cut so precisely that not even a hair could be slipped between them.

GIZA PLATEAU

Though many stones clearly came from the surrounding area, some stones were moved from as far away as 600 miles. How could mere humans have dragged such stones across the scorching desert and then placed them with such astonishing accuracy? The workers probably used barges, sledges, levers, rollers, inclined planes, and reed ropes to

painstakingly coax the massive stones into position. It was a feat unequaled in its time.

Within the Great Pyramid there is a central chamber that shelters an empty rose-colored granite sarcophagus, which is a large stone coffin. The coffin probably once held the remains of Cheops (also known as Khufu), who ruled Egypt between 2789 and 2767 B.C. But when the tomb was opened in the ninth century, the body was gone. It's likely that it had been plundered by grave robbers.

To prevent it from being plundered, the King's Chamber of Cheops was constructed near the heart of the pyramid about 140 feet above the desert floor. The gallery adjoining the chamber had slanting floors, above which huge blocks of stone were braced by timbers. When the pharaoh's mummified body was safe inside the chamber, the timbers were removed and the blocks slid into place, sealing the tomb. Unfortunately, it seems this was not enough to save the tomb of Cheops from thieves.

Did the empty sarcophagus found in the central chamber of the Great Pyramid once hold the remains of Cheops, who ruled Egypt from 2789 to 2767 B.C.?

The Mound Builders

The air was cool, crisp, and quite still. A man stood on the lofty, odd-shaped earthen mound surveying the lightly forested Ohio countryside below. All at once, an eerie feeling crept over him. As he watched, shivering, leaves began to flutter and swirl upward. His horror mounted as he somehow sensed an evil, invisible force moving closer. Then the leaves dropped to the ground. Nothing stirred. Whatever had been responsible for the disturbance was gone. The man, sociology professor Robert Harner, described the sensation as "the coldest, most abject terror I have ever experienced." This occurred in 1976 at the Serpent Mound in Adams County, Ohio.

The Serpent Mound is an example of huge earthworks, or earthen mounds, constructed by a group of mystical

Constructed by the first of the Mound Builders, the Adena People, the Serpent Mound is 1,348 feet long and is in the form of a snake with a gaping mouth.

Native American cultures known collectively as the Mound Builders. The mysterious 2,500-year-old Serpent Mound is 1,348 feet long, and is in the form of a snake with a gaping mouth. A smaller, egg-shaped mound is gripped in its jaws. It

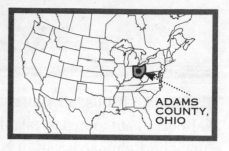

ADAMS COUNTY, OHIO

was made by the first of the Mound Builders, the Adena People.

The Adena were very different from other Native Americans who lived in the Ohio Valley. The custom that truly set them apart was how they buried their dead. Bodies were placed in log tombs with objects of silver, copper, and more. The tombs were burned immediately afterward and covered with earth. Others were built above them, and so the burial mounds grew. Many Adena burial mounds have been found, some in the shape of lizards, turtles, bears, birds, and panthers.

The Hopewell Indians prospered in the Illinois Valley around the first century A.D. They soon spread into the Ohio Valley, and like the Adenas, they too built mounds in animal shapes. Bodies were often buried where the heart of the animal would be. Like many Native American cultures, the Hopewells believed that their religious leaders, or shamans, transformed themselves into animals, and that the animals' spirits protected the mounds. Perhaps that explains what Robert Harner sensed that day as he stood on the Serpent Mound.

The Mississippians flourished around the ninth century A.D. The most famous Mississippian site is a tremendous settlement known as Cahokia, near what is now St. Louis, Illinois. Cahokia included about 100 mounds and may once have had a population of about 40,000 people. Many of these mounds can be seen today.

53

Vanished

In the late 1500s, Sir Walter Raleigh of England attempted to establish a British colony on Roanoke Island in North Carolina. Because of the harsh conditions, the first settlement was unsuccessful and the colonists returned to England. Another small group, also under Raleigh and the British crown, was killed by hostile Indians. In 1587, 112 colonists arrived and established a small village. The group worked hard to build shelters and prepare for the upcoming winter. In August, their leader, John White, sailed to England for more supplies with a crew of 15 men. He intended to return in the spring, but England and Spain went to war, which prevented White from sailing back to Roanoke until 1590, three years later.

When he finally landed on the tiny island, White found the colony eerily quiet. The ruins of a hastily built fortress and a few other dwellings still stood, but the only trace of the colonists was a single clue: The word *CROATOAN* had been carved in a doorpost. As soon as possible,

The word CROATOAN carved in a doorpost was perhaps the only clue to the mysterious disappearance of 112 English settlers on Roanoke Island.

an expedition was formed to go to nearby Croatoan Island, home of the Hatteras Indians. That expedition (and the four that followed) failed to turn up the missing colonists. In 1603, the search was abandoned, and the fate of the colonists remains a mystery to this day. Some people say that perhaps they made a new life for themselves and did not want to be found.

In the eighteenth century, however, settlers along the Lumber River in North Carolina came in contact with a group of Native Americans, the Lumbee of Robeson County, who spoke a language remarkably similar in many ways to English. Although Native Americans generally have dark hair, eyes, and complexions, many Lumbee Indians have light hair and eyes and fair complexions.

It seems that in about 1650, many of the Hatteras tribe of Croatoan moved to the mainland of North Carolina to the

ROANOKE ISLAND

Lumber River Valley. They were the ancestors of the current Lumbee Indians. Of the 95 surnames listed for the colonists at Roanoke, 41 are surnames of members of the Lumbee Tribe. Some people think that many of the Lumbee may be descendants of the English colonists who disappeared in 1590.

Bigfoot

When European settlers arrived in the American Pacific Northwest, the Karok Indians related tales of a bizarre apelike creature that lived in the woods. The Indians of British Columbia, Canada, called it *Sasquatch*, which means "wild man of the woods." Today, in northern California, Oregon, and Washington, it is better known as Bigfoot.

In 1958, bulldozer operator Jerry Crew found peculiar tracks around his camp in Humboldt County, northern California. The humanlike prints were about 16 inches long, 7 inches wide, and very deep. Since then, hundreds of similar tracks have been found

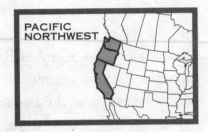

throughout the Pacific Northwest. There have also been hundreds of reported sightings of Bigfoot, from alarming tales of attacks by half-human, half-ape monsters to eyewitness descriptions of large apelike animals some eight feet tall.

The most famous is the Patterson/Gimlin sighting, because the two men supposedly managed to get the creature on film. Roger Patterson and Bob Gimlin were in Bluff Creek Valley, northeast of Eureka, California, on October 20, 1967, when they allegedly saw Bigfoot. They claimed it was a female, about seven feet tall, and covered with dark inch-long hair. Later, the men allowed a panel of scientists to view

Hundreds of humanlike footprints, some measuring 16 inches long and 7 inches wide, have been discovered throughout the Pacific Northwest.

the film, and although some felt it was quite interesting, others pointed out that it could easily be an actor in a suit rather than a real Bigfoot. Nevertheless, some very reputable people, including police officers and forest rangers, also have claimed that Bigfoot is real.

How is it possible that an 8-foot-tall, 500-pound being could go undetected? There is still plenty of wild, unexplored forest in the Pacific Northwest, but it seems that something—perhaps identifiable droppings, bones, or carcasses—should have been found. Believers suggest that the creatures might actually bury their dead, making the remains nearly impossible to find. So the mystery endures, and Bigfoot continues to dwell somewhere between legend and reality.

All in the Family

Bigfoot isn't the only giant apelike creature people have claimed to see. In Asia, high in the rugged mountains known as the Himalayas, the people of Nepal tell of a race of ape-people called Yeti. Westerners have come to call them Abominable Snowmen. In 1832, B. H. Hodson, an Englishman living in Nepal, claimed he saw a huge dark-haired beast walking upright across a snowy ledge. In 1951, a British explorer named Eric Shipton took photographs of unusual human-like footprints in the snow in the Gauri Sankar range of the Himalayas. The prints were 13 inches long and 8 inches wide—far too big to have been made by a human. Many Nepalese guides tell stories of Yeti, but to this day there is no solid proof that such creatures actually exist.

Machu Picchu is considered the most spectacular ruin in all of South America. So why did its inhabitants abandon this magnificent city without leaving so much as a trace?

Machu Picchu

"I began to realize that this wall with its adjoining semi-circular temple . . . [was] as fine as the finest stonework in the world. It fairly took my breath away."

This was written in 1912 by Hiram Bingham, a professor at Yale University, when he stumbled upon the forgotten city of Machu Picchu. He was exploring Peru when a peasant told him of a lost city nearby. Bingham offered the man several coins to take him there, and the needy Peruvian quickly accepted.

In the rain, Bingham set out on the danger-ous climb with only his guide and a bodyguard. About 1,500 feet up the mountain, they came to the hut of a Peruvian family. The peasant would go no farther, so Bingham continued the rest of the way guided by a little boy not yet 10 years old.

What Bingham saw when he reached the top of the steep pinnacle amazed him. Massive stone walls, elaborate terraces, step-pyramid plat-forms, dozens of roofless buildings—it was Machu Picchu, the forgotten home of a vanished people!

Perched atop a remote cliff on the eastern slope of the Andes Mountains, Machu Picchu is shrouded in mystery. It is 8,530 feet above sea level and hidden from view like an eagle's nest. With its 3,000-step temple and other complex structures (many of which still stand), Machu Picchu is considered the most spectacular archaeological ruin in all of South America. Beautiful gardens, terraces, ceremonial palaces,

59

aqueducts, and fountains at one time filled the city, which was built by the Incas, a large tribe of South American Indians.

But how were they able to accomplish such a masterful technological feat? Machu Picchu's many buildings were constructed of immense white granite blocks that were cut to fit so perfectly that no mortar was ever needed to hold them together. Even today, a knife blade cannot be wedged between them. It seems incredible that the Incas could have produced masonry of such size and precision, much less transport it from rock quarries. Why? Because they had only simple stone tools, no wheels, and no draft animals such as horses to help with the labor.

In the 1500s, the Inca's land, which is now Peru, was conquered by Spaniards. Unlike other Inca cities, Machu Picchu shows no evidence of having been captured or even visited by the conquerors. So why did the Incas abandon their great city? Perhaps that's the greatest mystery of all.

England's Most Haunted House

On a cool April night in 1916, Edward Cooper glanced out his window and saw two lights moving across the meadow from Borley Rectory toward his cottage. In the moonlight, Cooper saw that they were the head-lamps on a black coach drawn by two speeding horses. As the coach raced closer, he was surprised to realize that it wasn't making a sound. But that wasn't the strangest part. To his astonishment, Cooper watched as the vehicle continued toward him, moving straight through concrete walls and hedges.

ESSEX, ENGLAND

This is only one of the dozens of tales about Borley Rectory, a grim Victorian build-ing that some psychic researchers once called "England's most haunted house." It was built in 1863, on the north bank of the Stour River in Essex, England, for Reverend Henry Bull and his family. Frightening things began to happen from the very first night the family moved in. One daughter was awakened by a slap in the face. Another saw a dark man in a tall hat standing in the doorway of her room. Others heard footsteps, voic-es, ringing bells, chanting, and organ music. Supposedly, a Benedictine abbey had once stood on the site.

The spirit most often seen was reportedly a phantom nun. According to one story, during the 17th century a French nun named Marie Lairre left her convent and came to England to marry a young man from an important family. Some say that she was strangled by her fiancé in a small building that would become part of the future rectory. Her body, so the story goes, was buried in the cellar of the building.

The ghost of Marie Lairre, a French nun who was reportedly murdered in the rectory in the 17th century, has been spotted roaming the grounds on numerous occasions.

In 1930, the Reverend Lionel Foyster, his young wife, Marianne, and his daughter, Adelaide, moved into the home. The activity then took a more sinister turn. Something unseen began to call Marianne's name and once physically attacked her. That wasn't all. Phantom writing appeared on scraps of paper and even on the walls, right before the eyes of astonished observers. One particular message was quite clear. In a wispy script it read: "Marianne, please get help."

After several years, the Foyster family had had enough of the rectory and moved out, leaving it empty. In 1937, Harry Price, founder of Britain's National Laboratory of Psychical Research, rented it. He invited a group of 10 people to stay on the premises, if they dared. The group experienced some unusual things, such as sudden drops in temperature, falling objects, and unexplained noises, but it seemed as if the hauntings were decreasing, compared with what occured during the Foyster occupancy.

In 1939, Borley Rectory mysteriously burned to the ground. Some say that strange lights can still be seen among the ruins. Was the rectory truly a link to the world beyond the grave? Did restless spirits actually roam its grounds? Or were the stories, such as the tale of the murdered nun, simply the products of over-active imaginations? Perhaps, but in 1943, the cellar at Borley Rectory was dug up. About four feet below the surface, diggers found pieces of a woman's skull and several pendants with religious symbols.

The Lost Dutchman's Mine

Deception, treachery, and a powerful curse all are a part of the legend of the Lost Dutchman's Mine. Although it is said to contain a fortune in gold, the Arizona mine also holds death and disaster for those who try to claim it.

The mysterious mine is mentioned in the records of Spanish monks who traveled to the area in the mid-1700s, and it later became part of a land grant to Don Miguel Peralta from King Ferdinand of Spain. In 1864, when Enrico Peralta, a descendant of Miguel's, took a small expedition to the area, he and his group were killed by Apaches. Although one man survived the battle and made his way back to Mexico with a map of the site, no one seemed interested, and the map disappeared.

ARIZONA

About 10 years later, two German men, Jacob Waltz and Jacob Weiser, supposedly rescued a man who was being beaten in a fight. The battered fellow claimed to be the son of Enrico Peralta, and for some unexplained reason he sold the rights to the family's ill-fated mine to the two Germans.

At first, Waltz and Weiser were able to work the site with no trouble from the Apaches. They actually uncovered a small fortune in gold nuggets, and even managed to keep the location of their bonanza a secret. But the curse of the mine finally caught up with them. Weiser disappeared, and all that Waltz found in camp were arrows and the fragment of a bloody shirt that had once been his partner's. Fearing for his life, Jacob Waltz abandoned the mine. When he died, he left behind no record of its location. People had mistaken Waltz's German accent for Dutch, so the lost treasure came to be known as the Lost Dutchman's Mine.

In spite of the obstacles, in about 1880 two men claimed to have once again discovered the site. They galloped into a town thought to be near the mine with their saddlebags filled with gold nuggets. Scoffing at warnings about the curse, they rode back for another load. The doomed men never returned. Their lifeless bodies were eventually discovered by a search party. And the human death toll rose higher still.

In 1931, a man named Adolph Ruth set out for the mountains carrying what he claimed was the original Peralta map once owned by Waltz. Since the Indians were long gone, Ruth felt that he had nothing to fear . . . but he was wrong. His headless corpse was eventually recovered where it had fallen. In his pocket was a scrap of paper on which Ruth had scribbled, "About 200 feet across from the cave," and the Latin words *Veni, Vidi, Vici,* for "I came, I saw, I conquered." Was this meant to be some sort of clue to the location of the mine? Is the treasure of the Lost Dutchman's Mine still buried somewhere in the mountains of Arizona? As yet, no one knows.

According to the legend, those who seek the fortune hidden within the mysterious mine may find more than just gold—death and despair!

Faces in the Floor

When something is buried, we expect it to stay hidden, but that is not always the case. In 1971, this became terrifyingly clear to a housewife in the village of Bélmez, in southern Spain.

The day began much like any other, but when Maria Pereira entered her kitchen, she was horrified to find a spectral image on the floor. It was the anguished face of a woman she had never seen before, seemingly etched in the pink tiles. Once she recovered from the surprise, Maria tried to scour the image away, but it wouldn't budge. In fact, the more she scrubbed, the more sorrowful the grimace on the face became.

BÉLMEZ,
SPAIN

The frightened housewife was unable to rid herself of the horror, so she had the entire floor pulled up and new concrete poured in its place. It did no good. Not only did the face return, but others showed up as well! Some would appear for only a short period. Others lasted for weeks, but their pitiful expressions would change over time. Before long, the word of the unusual "haunting" spread. Mrs. Pereira permitted scientists to seal off her kitchen in the hopes of discovering the key to the mystery.

The investigators began by fitting a large plastic plate to the floor to be sure that no one was secretly drawing the phantom faces. Next, they removed a section of tile, and the images were chemically tested. In 1974, one scientist actually watched as a new face slowly formed. He was even able to photograph it.

When there was no other way to find out why the faces were emerging on her kitchen floor, Mrs. Pereira allowed the scientists to pry up the tiles and dig out the soil underneath. It wasn't long before they made a startling discovery: dozens of bones—very old human bones—buried beneath the Pereiras' kitchen.

The remains were far too old to identify, so the mystified researchers had no choice but to give up and replace the floor. The faces continued to appear on the new floor for a while. Then, one day, the phenomenon simply ended.

A Grave Mistake

There is some evidence that the Pereira house was built over an ancient cemetery. The bodies discovered beneath the floor may have been those of 11th-century martyrs killed by Moorish invaders, or innocent victims who had been executed for witchcraft. When one expert made tapes in the kitchen using microphones designed to detect sounds beyond the range of human hearing, the researchers heard moans and tormented voices wailing in unknown languages.

The anguished faces staring up from Maria Pereira's kitchen floor were too horrifying for the housewife to bear. But when she had the entire floor replaced, the faces returned!

El Panteón Cemetery Guanajuato, Mexico

"**H**ere it is!" the man exclaimed, stabbing a finger in his guidebook. "El Panteón Cemetery, and it's less than a mile from here."

"Great!" said the man's wife. "We can see the mummies before it gets dark."

The young American couple left the café and began walking down the street under the dying Mexican sunlight. Chatting as they went, their arms interlocked, they were utterly oblivious to the gruesome, terrifying display they were about to encounter.

Every year thousands of thrill seekers make their way through the catacombs, or underground passages, at El Panteón Cemetery in

GUANAJUATO, MEXICO

Guanajuato, Mexico. For a nominal fee they can view the more than one hundred mummies on display there—bodies that were originally buried in the cemetery directly above but were exhumed from their graves when families or friends could no longer afford to pay for grave maintenance. Because of the extremely dry Mexican climate and the high amount of salt in the soil, the bodies have not decomposed. Instead they have been preserved in all their otherworldy horror.

The mummies of Guanajuato have existed since before the turn of the century. Back then, however, it would have been hard to imagine that so revolting a scene would one day become a macabre tourist attraction. But that's precisely what has happened.

When you descend the stairway to the catacombs, you come to a vaulted corridor where the mummies (which, incidentally, are not wrapped in gauze like the ones in the movies) are on display. There, you are free to examine their withered remains up close—if you have the stomach for it. In the well-lighted corridor you will see the mummies standing or sitting in dreadful silence behind their individual glass coffins. Some of them reach out with open arms as if pleading. Others appear to be struggling, as though they were trying to break out of their confinement.

But it's the faces of the mummies which, once seen, become imprinted in people's minds forever. The awful, empty eyesockets seem to stare directly at you. The skeletal mouths hang open in silent but eternal screams, revealing long incisors that look more like fangs than human teeth. Some of the mummies wear shoes and have facial hair, with remnants of burial clothes drapped over their parched and withering remains.

One thing is certain: No one—not even the most die-hard horror buff—can be too prepared for what awaits them in the catacombs beneath El Panteón Cemetery.

Every year thousands of thrill seekers pay to view the gruesome mummies on display in the catacombs beneath El Panteón Cemetery.

Komodo Island
Lesser Sundas, Indonesia

The huge creature has an armor-plated head and large, razor-sharp claws. Its thick, forked tongue flickers in and out of its open mouth. The massive body, with its short, thick tail, is more than ten feet long and weighs over two hundred pounds.

The creature is a Komodo Dragon, the world's largest monitor lizard, so called because they supposedly warn crocodiles of the approach of man. Several thousand of them wander freely on Komodo Island as well as parts of the Indonesian islands Rintja, Padar, and Flores.

These isolated islands provide an ideal habitat for the Komodo dragon, consisting of monsoon forests and savannah grasslands where game is plentiful. They feed on the dead and rotted flesh of goats, wild pigs, water buffalo, rusa deer, and feral horses. The giant lizard has even been known to feed on human corpses if given the opportunity.

Although it is believed that Komodo dragons reaching twenty feet or more in length do exist on the island, the largest that have actually been observed are about ten feet long. These large lizards are very dangerous and will attack and eat any smaller

creatures they can corner. The large moni-
tors are not very fast, and most humans
can outrun them. Some people, however,
have not been so fortunate.

According to a 1972 article by Walter
Auffenberg in the magazine *Natural
History,* "People have been bitten in the shoulder or neck as they slept on
the ground during the daytime. Others were attacked from behind while
working in the bush." One person died in an unprovoked attack by a
Komodo dragon, while another succumbed to a bacterial infection of bite
wounds inflicted by the large lizard.

Auffenberg found that most of the huge monitor lizards avoided
contact with humans, but some were very aggressive, entering tents and
shelters and attacking people. Needless to say, residents of the island are
always on the alert for these giant creatures!

Who said dinosaurs are extinct? On Komodo Island, the past merges
with the present in the form of these remarkable, dangerous, and frightening
creatures.

*It is believed that some Komodo
dragons reach twenty feet
or more in length.*

Devil's Hole
Niagara Gorge, New York

- ☉ June 28, 1854—A five-year-old girl falls 150 feet to her death near the cave known as Devil's Hole.
- ☉ September 6, 1901—President William McKinley rides the Great Gorge Railroad past Devil's Hole and hours later is hit by an assassin's bullet. He dies eight days later.
- ☉ March 12, 1907—Just past Devil's Hole, a sheet of ice crushes a railroad conductor to death. He had stepped out of his train to throw a switch on the tracks.
- ☉ February 27, 1913—The body of a sixty-five-year-old man is found fifty feet below the cliff at Devil's Hole.
- ☉ July 1, 1917—A railroad car near Devil's Hole derails and plunges into the river below, killing fourteen and injuring twenty-eight.
- ☉ June 7, 1929—A train near Devil's Hole strikes an elderly man and knocks him into the river, where he is swept away.
- ☉ September 5, 1932—A fourteen-year-old boy falls to his death on the railroad tracks near Devil's Hole.
- ☉ 1935—The Great Gorge Railroad route, which passes Devil's Hole, is abandoned when a five-thousand-ton avalanche uproots the tracks.

Author Dwight Whalen investigated the history of Devil's Hole cave and documented the bad luck and misfortune listed above in an article in *Fate* magazine in June 1992. Whalen discovered that over the years the cave and nearby area have seen more than their share of violent incidents that resulted in death, destruction, and injury.

Devil's Hole cave extends approximately twenty feet deep into the rock, about three miles below Niagara Falls and high above the whirling waters of Devil's Hole Rapids in the Niagara Gorge. A large boulder called Ambush Rock stands in front of the cave opening and was once thought to have completely covered the entrance.

NIAGARA GORGE, NEW YORK

Stories about the cave originated hundreds of years ago when ancient Seneca Indians in the Niagara region believed the cave to be the home of the devil. They called it the "abode of the Evil Spirit" and avoided the area so as not to disturb the demon within.

The Indians warned French explorer Robert La Salle not to enter the cave in 1669, but he wandered inside to investigate anyway. According to E. T. Williams' *History of Niagara County,* "His many misfortunes thereafter and his assassination later in Texas were attributed by the Senecas to the evil spirit he had antagonized by invading its domain."

On September 14, 1763, a convoy of British soldiers was attacked and massacred by Indians as it was passing Devil's Hole. Most of the nearly one hundred men were killed and then scalped. Some jumped to their death over the cliff to avoid the Indians. Only three survived the attack.

The awful noises of the massacre were heard by soldiers lower down in the gorge, and two companies came to the convoy's aid. These soldiers were also ambushed by the Indians and nearly all were killed. Although accounts differ, it is believed that nearly two hundred men were murdered that day near Devil's Hole.

It is said that the stream that runs through the ravine near the cave ran red with the blood of the victims of the Indians and is called Bloody Run even today. For many years after the Devil's Hole Massacre, remains such as human bones, pieces of wagons, and parts of guns were found strewn among the rocks in the gorge below the cave.

Whalen noted accidents and mishaps associated with Devil's Hole over the past fifty years. In 1949 a woman fell off the cliff but survived to tell the tale. In 1971 a man fell and broke his ankle. In 1982 two young men were attacked and injured by unknown assailants. That same year a fifteen-foot boulder crashed down into the gorge, narrowly missing a twenty-five-year-old man. In 1984 another man fell and was hospitalized with head and chest injuries. In 1987 two men in separate incidents were drowned in the river below Devil's Hole. No one knows how many additional cases were not reported or overlooked throughout the years.

Why are there so many accidents and tragedies associated with this gloomy, dark cave? Are the Indian legends true? Is Devil's Hole the home of an evil spirit or demon? Is there a curse on some of those who enter or venture nearby? Do deaths or injuries appease the demon for a number of years until the next incident?

Some say that the winding pathways and rocky cliffs make Devil's Hole the dangerous spot that it is. They say that accidents can and do happen—and they seem to occur very often at Devil's Hole!

There are others who wonder whether those who mysteriously lost their footing near the cave or were involved in accidents or mishaps were really controlled or affected by certain supernatural forces. Is it a curse or just a string of coincidences? Is it an evil spirit or just careless accidents?

Care to find out for yourself? Don't forget to bring your rabbit's foot!

Berry Pomeroy Castle
Devon, England

In the late nineteenth century the famous English physician Sir Walter Farquhar visited the seriously ill wife of the steward (manager) of Berry Pomeroy Castle for the second day in a row. Worried about her condition, Sir Walter was both surprised and pleased to see that his patient was much improved.

After some conversation with the steward, the doctor mentioned a lovely stranger he saw the previous day while waiting to examine his patient. "I was sitting in the oak-paneled room with the loft when the door opened and in walked a remarkably beautiful young woman dressed in white," Sir Walter related. "She was wringing her hands and obviously very upset, then she glanced at me and disappeared up the stairs."

After hearing these words, the steward turned pale and began to pace the floor nervously.

"Are you all right? Did I say something wrong?" asked the concerned Sir Walter.

DEVON, ENGLAND

"What you saw was a ghost," the man replied in a murmer. "She was the daughter of a former owner of the castle."

"You're joking, of course," said Sir Walter. "Just who was she?"

"She's a ghost, all right. Little is known of her, but she was said to be as cruel and wicked as she was beautiful." The anguished steward sat down and placed his head in his hands. "Her appearance always is followed by the death of someone connected to the castle." Then the steward began to sob. "My wife, my wife."

"Get a hold of yourself," Sir Walter exclaimed. "You surely don't

An appearance by the ghostly lady in white was once said to foreshadow the death of someone connected to the castle.

believe that! Your wife is much better today and soon she'll be up and about."

The man shook his head. "The ghost was last seen here before my son drowned in an accident."

"Just a coincidence," Sir Walter replied. "You'll see. Your wife has improved remarkably."

Several hours later the steward's wife died suddenly and mysteriously, just as her husband had feared.

Shaken by the sudden turn of events, Sir Walter Farquhar was now convinced he had seen the ghost of the beautiful woman in white and wrote about his encounter in his published memoirs.

Feelings of intense dread, loneliness, and evil are how some visitors describe their experiences at the ruins of Berry Pomeroy Castle. Reports of hauntings can be traced back hundreds of years to the de la Pomerai family, who resided in the castle from 1066 to 1548. After it was sold, the new owners, the Seymours, built a large mansion within the castle walls, which was abandoned in the middle seventeenth century due to damage from the English Civil War. Further deterioration occurred in the early eighteenth century from a fire.

In addition to the ghost of the evil woman in white, visitors over the last fifty years have seen two other ghosts at the castle. Margaret de Pomeroy is said to walk the castle's ramparts in flowing white robes, calling on those she sees to come join her. Apparently Margaret was imprisoned in the castle dungeon and was starved to death by her sister Eleanor de Pomeroy. Both Eleanor and Margaret loved the same man, and Eleanor was jealous of her beautiful sister.

Consider for a moment the cruel and evil history of Pomeroy Castle. Is it any wonder that visitors leave the grounds with strong feelings of dread and terror?

Salem, Massachusetts

Descending the steps of the Witch Dungeon Museum in Salem, Massachusetts, the words *creepy* and *scary* immediately come to mind. It's dark, damp, and cold here, probably just the way it was more than three hundred years ago during the famous Salem witchcraft trials.

In 1692 a group of impressionable teenage girls claimed they had been bewitched by various members of the community. The girls exhibited bizarre behavior: barking, screaming, choking, and hysteria. They accused many of the older and respected Salem women of witchcraft, claiming to have seen them meeting with the devil.

The only evidence against the accused was what the magistrates called "spectral evidence," which basically meant anything that the girls said. If they said you met with the devil, whether you denied it or not, you were guilty. The accused women were subsequently subjected to a body search for the devil's mark. Often a common birthmark or mole was considered proof of witchcraft.

SALEM, MASSACHUSETTS

If a woman was lucky enough to have a body free of blemishes, she was brought to court to confront the girls, who screamed and convulsed in her presence. It was believed that touching a witch would make her powerless, so each girl was forced to touch the accused, and lo and behold, the girls suddenly calmed down and acted normally. The magistrates took this as additional spectral evidence.

Before the witchcraft hysteria ended, nineteen people had been hanged and numerous others were imprisoned. The hysterical girls held in their hands the power of life and death in Salem, but when they accused the governor's wife of being a witch, they had gone too far. The governor ordered the so-called witches to be freed and the trials ended.

Scene after scene of the witch trials is depicted in the Witch Dungeon

Museum. But it is the one of Giles Corey and the awful way he died that is both fascinating and repulsive to visitors. Author Robert Cahill in his book *Haunted Happenings* calls Corey's death "the most tragic and brutal murder in the name of justice ever performed in America and certainly the most terrible in New England."

Giles Corey was one of several men accused of being a witch. Corey kept silent during his trial, determined to show contempt for the girls. According to the law back then, a person could not be tried if he or she didn't enter a plea, but there was a penalty for remaining mute: being slowly crushed under weights until the accused either pleaded or died. Once the person pleaded one way or the other, he or she was imprisoned and their money and property confiscated by the sheriff.

On September 19, 1692, the eighty-year-old man was stripped, taken to an open field near the jail, and made to lie down in a pit. As depicted in the museum scene, a large piece of wood was laid across his chest. As more and more rocks were placed on the board, the sheriff cried "Confess" over and over again. The weight increased and Corey's eyes and tongue bulged out of his face, but still the old man kept silent. Just before he died, Giles Corey supposedly called out, "I curse you and Salem!"

Many believe that the ghost of Giles Corey haunts the old burial ground near the jail in Salem where he died. An increase in sightings of Corey's ghost has also been noted right before a major disaster or setback to the town. The most famous was the Great Fire of 1914, which destroyed one-third of the city.

Just a coincidence? Possibly, but it's best not to stand too long in front of the scene of Giles Corey's death at the Witch Dungeon Museum. That feeling of a cold, spindly hand on your shoulder may not be just a figment of your imagination.

The East Coast of Australia off New South Wales and Queensland

The two honeymooners were scuba diving in Byron Bay, a popular beach area 370 miles north of Sydney, the capital of the Australian state of New South Wales. Married less than three weeks, Debbie and John Ford swam in beautiful clear water at a depth of about forty feet on June 9, 1993.

Suddenly John saw a huge, menacing shadow gliding beneath the surface of the water and heading toward his wife. John knew his wife was in great danger, so he swam between her and the advancing creature. Seconds later a sixteen-foot great white shark grabbed John in its huge jaws and began shaking him violently before taking him below the surface to his death. Debbie's life, however, had been spared.

Only four days earlier a thirty-four-year-old woman was attacked in another area off the eastern Australian coast and carried away by a twelve-foot great white shark. The attack was witnessed by her husband and five young children. The only remains recovered was a severed human leg with a diving fin still attached.

The east coast of Australia has had more shark attacks and fatalities than any part of the world, yet compared to other causes of death—like traffic accidents or disease—the risk to swimmers and scuba divers is still very minimal. Keep repeating that over and over again while you're splashing around in the waters off eastern Australian beaches!

The east coast of Australia has had more shark attacks than any other part of the world.

George Burgess, director of the International Shark Attack File, which keeps records of all reported shark attacks, wrote that "worldwide there are probably fifty to seventy-five shark attacks annually, resulting in about five to ten deaths." He declared that "many more people are injured and killed on land while driving to and from the beach than by sharks in the water."

The risk may be minimal, but that doesn't make the prospect of a shark attack any less unnerving. Great white sharks can grow to twenty-five or more feet in length and weigh several thousand pounds. Their terrifying

QUEENSLAND, NEW SOUTH WALES, AUSTRALIA

mouths, lined from front to back with razor-sharp teeth, are huge enough to swallow a person whole. These sharks are eating machines and will devour almost anything, including each other.

If the hairs on your neck aren't standing straight up from the very possibility of a shark attack, keep your eyes peeled for the beautiful but lethal Australian sea wasp, the most venomous jellyfish in the world. There are signs on certain eastern Australian beaches that read, "Warning—Sea Wasps Are Deadly in These Waters Between October and May."

Brush up against the transparent tentacles of the sea wasp and you'll experience terrible pain, partial paralysis, massive welts on the skin, and possible death within a few minutes. This lovely little creature has caused the deaths of sixty-six people off Queensland since 1880. Numerous others have survived the ordeal, often with lasting scars and very bad memories.

Regardless of the risks that may exist, more people than ever flock to the picturesque beaches of Australia's eastern coast for a day of fun in the sun and surf. After all, the odds are definitely in their favor.

Care to take a dip?

The Tomb of Tutankhamen Valley of the Kings, near Luxor, Egypt

"Death comes on wings to he who enters the tomb of a pharaoh."

Some say archaeologist Howard Carter found this warning on a tablet of hieroglyphics in the outer chamber of the tomb of the pharaoh Tutankhamen, which he discovered in 1923. Supposedly Carter took the tablet away before his workers could see the warning and become alarmed.

Others say it comes from a letter to the London *Times* written by novelist Marie Corelli in March of 1923. She quoted this phrase from an ancient Arabic book and predicted the death of those working in the tomb. Few in the press took note of her prophecy.

Several days after the letter appeared Lord Carnarvon, Carter's long-time financial sponsor, died unexpectedly of an infected insect bite that turned into pneumonia. Commenting on Carnarvon's death, Sir Arthur Conan Doyle, author and creator of Sherlock Holmes, said he believed that the death resulted from the pharaoh's revenge. From then on the "curse of Tutankamen" made front page news.

Archaeologist Howard Carter's amazing discovery occurred six hundred miles up the river Nile near the town of Luxor in the Valley of the Kings. Here, more than three thousand years ago, the pharaohs of ancient Egypt were buried in magnificent hidden tombs.

Carter's find was considered the archaeological event of the century. First his workers unearthed a steep cut in the rock and then the upper edges of a stairway. Even today, descending the sixteen steps that lead into an underground passage ten feet high and six feet wide, and then through doorways into chamber after chamber, one feels as if the past and present have merged together. It's a strange and frightening feeling.

"For the moment, time as a factor in human life . . . lost its meaning," wrote Carter. "Three thousand, four thousand years . . . have passed and gone. . . . The very air you breathe, unchanged throughout the centuries, you share with those who laid the mummy to its rest. . . . You feel an intruder. . . ."

When Carter and Lord Carnarvon entered the pharaoh's outer rooms and burial chamber, they came upon riches and treasure beyond imagination—golden couches, statues, gold- and jewel-covered chariots, all stored within the pharaoh's tomb to help him complete his afterlife journey into paradise.

The mummy itself was placed in three coffins, one inside the other. The two outer coffins were made of wood and covered with gold and jewels. The inner coffin was made of solid gold and weighed nearly three thousand pounds, requiring four men to lift it. The twenty-one-inch solid gold funeral mask covering the mummy's face was an exact likeness of the seventeen-year-old boy-king.

But Lord Carnarvon hardly had a chance to share in these fabulous discoveries. He died suddenly at the age of fifty-seven. One newspaper wrote that Carnarvon cut his finger on a poisonous object in the tomb. Another reported that at the exact moment of his death (2:00 A.M.) at the Continental Hotel in Cairo, the whole city was immersed in the blackness of a power failure. Some said it was just a coincidence, that Cairo was often subject to blackouts. Meanwhile, at his home in England, Carnarvon's dog reportedly began to bark and howl at the moment of his passing, and the dog itself died soon after. Was it the curse or just another coincidence?

TOMB OF TUTANKHAMEN, LUXOR, EGYPT

According to the *Atlas of the Supernatural* by Derek and Julia Parker, an American archaeologist, an American financier, a British industrialist, and the radiologist who x-rayed the body of Tutankhamen all died mysteriously after visiting the tomb. Within seven years, twenty-two people connected with the tomb's discovery were dead.

Yet Howard Carter lived until 1939 when he died at the age of sixty-six, and Dr. Douglas Derry, who dissected the pharaoh's mummy, lived to be over eighty! One theory states that a type of airborne bacteria or virus purposely placed in the tomb by ancient Egyptians may have affected some people and not others, since most of those who died exhibited symptoms of depression, numbness, and lethargy. Were Carter and Derry immune to the curse? Perhaps.

In the 1960s the treasures of the tomb of Tutankhamen were placed in a traveling exhibit that visited major cities throughout the world. The tour was coordinated by the director-general of the Antiquities Department of the Cairo Museum, where the valuable collection is usually displayed. The fifty-two-year-old Director-General, Gemal Mehrez, told one reporter, "I've been involved with tombs and mummies of pharaohs all my life. I'm living proof that it was all coincidence!"

A month later Mehrez was dead.

Bracken Cave near San Antonio, Texas

"What is that?" the man said, pointing to a dark mass in the distance. It was an early August evening in central Texas.

"It almost looks like a tornado funnel," said his wife, "but that's impossible. The weather here is calm and beautiful. There's not a cloud in the sky."

The man studied the shadowy formation. "I've never seen a funnel like that before, swirling around so high. It's almost as if it were . . ,"

"Alive," whispered the woman quietly.

The man turned to look at his wife and saw fear, as well as wonder and curiosity, in her face.

SAN ANTONIO, TEXAS

"Swarms of birds?" the man asked with a frown on his face.

"Bats!" cried his wife. "I remember reading about it in the guidebook. They're bats emerging from their cave to find food!"

The man shuddered. *Millions of bats,* he repeated to himself, then shot a quick glance at his wife. "Let's get back to San Antonio."

Beginning in the spring more than twenty million Mexican free-tailed bats emerge daily from Bracken Cave before sundown. Located less than twenty miles from downtown San Antonio, this huge cave is home to the largest bat colony in the world.

The huge flocks of bats climb as high as eleven thousand feet to catch tailwinds that carry them long distances at speeds of more than sixty miles per hour. In one single night's feeding these bats eat three to four billion insects. One bat alone can catch five hundred mosquito-sized insects in sixty minutes!

The colony from Bracken Cave consumes about two hundred and fifty tons of insects each and every night, so it's not surprising that the city and suburbs of San Antonio depend upon the bats for insect control. Their nightly trips for food lessen the need for chemical pesticides in the entire central Texas region.

During the day the roof of Bracken Cave is completely covered with 240 tons of resting bats that are hanging upside down. They produce enormous amounts of droppings, which accumulate on the cave floor to become what is known as guano. This rich layer of fertilizer is covered with millions of carnivorous beetles. If a young bat learning to fly makes an unexpected landing on the cave floor, the beetles can reduce it to bones within minutes.

Emergency landings seldom occur, since the bat maneuvers in the dark by the use of ultrasonic vibrations (called *echolocation*). These signals generate echoes in the form of high frequency sounds that enable the bat to be guided at night and to detect prey. In total darkness a bat can detect objects as fine as a human hair.

Just the thought of so many bats together in one place may make some people weak in the knees. Yet these creatures are harmless to man. Of the nearly one thousand types of bats in existence, only the vampire bats of Mexico and Central and South America are capable of passing diseases on to animals and occasionally man, and only a very small portion actually do so.

Bracken Cave is owned and protected by Bat Conservation International (BCI). The cave is not accessible to the public at the present time, but the incredible scene of the bats leaving the cave before sundown each day is visible many miles away.

For some it's a frightening and creepy sight, even a haunting experience. If you can manage to control the shudder of fear, it's a vision you'll never forget.

Bracken Cave is home to the largest bat colony in the world.

Csejthe Castle
Carpathian Mountains,
Hungary

Are those dark spots on the castle walls bloodstains? Or are they just blackened soot from the destructive fire caused by lightning in the eighteenth century? Is your feeling of dread and foreboding all in your mind?

You don't have to be psychic to pick up the loathsome vibrations at Csejthe Castle. The ruins of this once massive, horror-filled fortress in the foothills of the Carpathian Mountains in Central Europe still stand today. High on the hilltop overlooking the village of Csejthe, the castle was once the home of Countess Elizabeth Báthory.

Often called the Vampire Lady or the Blood Countess, Báthory was responsible for the murders of an astonishing 650 young women in the late sixteenth and early seventeenth centuries. If craving blood is the primary distinctive characteristic of a vampire, then Elizabeth Báthory had to be the most notorious human vampire in history.

Báthory was a wealthy and beautiful woman from one of Europe's great aristocratic families. She was a devoted wife to Count Ferencz Nadasdy and a loving mother to her four children. But she had two unusual and bizarre obsessions: Báthory was preoccupied with maintaining her beauty and youthful appearance, and she took pleasure in inflicting pain on people.

With the death of her husband in 1604, Báthory's obsessions quickly degenerated into complete madness. She began to believe that bathing in and drinking the blood of young, attractive girls would help to maintain her beauty. Indulging her gruesome habits on a daily basis required a steady stream of unsuspecting young girls. Most were lured to the castle under false pretenses. Few were ever seen alive again.

Disposing of the victims' bodies was a time-consuming and difficult task for Báthory's servants. Most were buried in nearby fields, but some were found by the villagers, who attributed the murders to vampires.

Over the years the unexplained disappearances and body count mounted, and the villagers began to talk. The Báthorys were powerful nobles, but it was hard for the people to ignore the screams coming from the castle night after night. Finally they banded together and denounced the countess to the king.

In 1611 an investigation of the murders led straight to Elizabeth Báthory. Austro-Hungarian high society was scandalized. They were especially horrified that Báthory had tortured and killed girls of noble birth as well as peasants.

Her servant accomplices were all tried and executed, but the countess' life was spared in order to avoid further disgrace to the illustrious Báthory and Nadasdy families. She was sentenced to imprisonment at Csejthe Castle for the rest of her life.

The king instructed workmen to wall up the windows and doors to Báthory's small room. Only an opening for food connected her to the outside world. A gallows was built at each of the four corners of the castle as a sign that justice had been done.

Elizabeth Báthory died alone after three and a half years in her tiny prison. Some believe her spirit lingers on, yearning for just one more bath of blood.

It's best not to stay too long in the ruins of Csejthe Castle, especially at dusk when the last light slips away. You just might see something that will haunt you for the rest of your life.

Old House Woods near Mathews Courthouse, Virginia

It stands now as it has stood for hundreds of years: a dark and gloomy pine forest quietly guarding its secrets from intruders. Located about four miles from the town of Mathews Courthouse, Virginia, the woods are less than a quarter mile from Chesapeake Bay.

"Old House Woods is haunted. I would advise you to stay away from there," declared local merchant Jesse V. Hudgins in 1926. "Probably there's gold buried there—lots of it. But for all I care, or anybody else that lives in the neighborhood, it can remain until the crack of doom."

Hudgins first confronted a ghostly resident of Old House Woods late one October night when he was seventeen years old. He was driving a wagon into town to get the doctor for a sick neighbor. As he neared the

MATHEWS COURTHOUSE, VIRGINIA

vacant and broken-down building known as the Old House, which stands by the side of the road and is surrounded by towering pines, he noticed a strange light in the woods moving in the same direction he was going.

"My horse, usually afraid of nothing, cowered and trembled violently," he explained. As Hudgins pulled even with the light, he saw a large man wearing a suit of armor and carrying a musket. What disturbed Hudgins was that the man was moving without making a sound, as if he were floating along the road instead of walking on it.

"My horse stopped dead still," recalled Hudgins.

When the figure stopped to face him, Hudgins stared back at the man and noticed that the woods behind him "became alive with lights and moving forms." Some of the figures carried guns or shovels while others dug near one of the trees.

"As my gaze returned to the first shadowy figure, what I saw was not the man in armor but a skeleton, and every bone of it was visible through the iron armor as if it were made of glass," Hudgins recalled. "The skull grinned at me horribly. Then, raising aloft a sword, which I had not . . . noticed, the awful specter started toward me menacingly."

Hudgins' terror was so great he felt his mind give way to unconsciousness. The next thing he knew he awoke in his bed surrounded by family members who told him he had been found on the road beyond Old House Woods. The horse, to the day it died, trembled and cowered whenever it approached the woods.

Some residents attribute the ghastly appearances to a band of pirates who used the woods to hide their booty but died in a dispute over how to divide the spoils.

A man named Harry Forrest, who lived six hundred feet from Old House Woods, saw and heard many strange things over the years: armies of marching British redcoats; moving lights and the sounds of digging; and a strange woman in white, whose appearance always signaled an upcoming storm.

There have been several attempts to dig for the buried treasure that most agree is hidden in Old House Woods, but all have resulted in tragedy or failure. One man disappeared; another was killed by lightning. The daughter of still another died mysteriously and suddenly.

It stands now as it will probably stand for another hundred years—dark, foreboding, and frightening, guarding its many secrets from intruders. Whoever walks in Old House Woods does so at his or her own risk.

The Tower of London
London, England

Terrified screams, headless ghosts, phantom figures, disappearing apparitions, floating heads—it's all routine at the Tower of London, historically one of the bloodiest spots in the world. In fact, the Tower is the oldest occupied building on earth today—older than the Vatican in Rome, the Louvre in Paris, and the Kremlin in Moscow.

LONDON, ENGLAND

The tower was used as a prison, complete with torture chamber and a place of execution, and hundreds of people were hanged or beheaded there. Their ghosts still frighten visitors and haunt the Tower grounds today.

The ghost most often seen by tourists and guards is that of Anne Boleyn, the second wife of King Henry VIII. Anne was beheaded in 1536 after she was found guilty of being unfaithful to the king. The real reason for her execution was that she couldn't bear Henry a son and heir to the throne. There was no such thing as a recognized divorce, and the king wanted to be free to take a new wife. Anne left her legacy in her daughter, Elizabeth I, who later became queen of England and reigned for forty-five years!

A small, pretty woman, Anne was terrified of being beheaded by an ax. Occasionally more than one blow was necessary to sever the head from the body, and it wasn't a particularly pleasant experience for the victim, the executioner, or the spectators. So she asked the king to allow her a quick death with a sword. The king agreed, and a Frenchman was brought over from Calais, a city in France, to perform the act.

On May 19, Anne was helped up the steps of the scaffold on the Tower grounds and knelt down in prayer. A bandage was placed over her eyes, and the executioner cut off her head with one sharp slice. Anne's ghost, with and without her head, has been seen alone or in a procession, usually close to the Bloody Tower, where she spent her last days.

One of the most horrible executions that occurred in the Tower of London was that of Margaret, the Countess of Salisbury, in 1541. The seventy-year-old noblewoman did not die with dignity. She was led screaming to the executioner's block, then escaped from the guards and ran around like a crazed maniac. The guards had to drag her back to the block and force her to bend down. Ax in hand, the executioner missed not once but *four* times, before the fifth blow finally severed her head from her body. Is it any wonder that Anne Boleyn wanted a skilled swordsman at her beheading? The countess Margaret's terrified screams are still heard near the site of her death on or near the anniversary of her execution.

There have always been ravens living on and around the grounds of the Tower of London. An old legend states that if the ravens leave, the Tower

Anne Boleyn, 2nd wife of Henry VIII, was beheaded in 1536, but her ghost—with or without her head— has been sighted frequently on the Tower grounds.

will fall and so will "the greatness and glory of Britain." Today six of these black birds have had their wings clipped so that they can't fly away.

Edgar Allan Poe once described ravens as "things of evil" and questioned whether they were birds or devils. It seems appropriate that these small, dark creatures inhabit a place that has seen so much horror.

Marfa, Texas

In 1883 Robert Ellison and several other cowboys were driving a herd of cattle across the desert area of Mitchell Flat between the small towns of Alpine and Marfa in southwestern Texas. They were camped for the night when Ellison noticed some peculiar balls of light at the base of the Chinati Mountains in the distance.

When he pointed them out to his companions, the men came up with a logical explanation. "They're just the lights from some Apache campfires," they explained.

But after watching them for a while, Ellison realized something scary and mysterious was happening. *Those are definitely not campfires,* he thought to himself. *Glowing balls of light . . . moving up and down and bouncing back and forth. What could possibly be doing that?*

The next morning Ellison and the others set out to find the Indian campfires and solve the mystery, but they found nothing at all. Speaking with others in the area, Ellison found that the local settlers had always seen strange lights flickering about and moving through the desert. But no one had any explanation as to what they were. Most people in the area just called them "ghost lights."

As the years passed and the lights near Marfa continued to appear, so did the sightings and the theories of explanation. Some researchers stated they were the headlights of cars reflected by the different temperature layers in the atmosphere. It sounds logical until you remember there were no car headlights when the lights were first sighted in the nineteenth century.

One scientist declared that the glowing balls of light were composed of electrically charged atomic particles. Others claimed they were a form of ball lightning, some type of electromagnetic energy, or even ionized gases escaping from faultlines in the earth. No theory has yet been proven to explain the strange and unusual lights.

Eyewitness accounts by those who have personally encountered the ghost lights make one wonder whether the supernatural rather than the scientific has something to do with this scary phenomenon.

One man traveling on Highway 90 west of Marfa saw the lights come up behind his truck and then disappear suddenly. Another man was frightened when a melon-sized ball of light stayed outside his car window for two miles no matter how fast he drove down the highway.

Two geologists documented their close encounters with the Marfa ghost lights in 1973. Pat Kenney and Elwood Wright observed the lights at a distance, swinging in an arc and turning completely around in a loop. "They appeared to be playing," said Kenney and Wright.

The two men wanted a closer look, so they drove onto Mitchell Flat along a dirt road toward the Chinati Mountains. Because of the full moon they drove without headlights for a while, then stopped and waited. Suddenly they saw two ghost lights about a thousand feet away moving no more than three or four feet above the ground.

The second light seemed slower than the first, so the men decided to sneak up as close to it as possible. The light, about one-half the size of a basketball, stopped in the air when they did, almost as if it knew exactly where they were and was daring them to follow. Both men felt sure the light possessed some type of intelligence. Wright stated later in a newspaper interview, "I really and truly don't have any idea what it was. It . . . looked like it was playing with us."

Are they trying to communicate something to us? If the answer is yes, what are they trying to tell us, and what is significant about Marfa, Texas, and other spots in the world where strange lights have been observed?

There are many questions, and nobody has the answers. In the meantime the ghost lights of Marfa, Texas, continue to amaze people and defy all explanation.

Marianas Trench off Guam, Pacific Ocean

Sea monsters, giant squids, monstrous eels, grotesque fish? What strange creatures lurk in the dark, cold, high-pressure depths of the ocean floor? Man has barely begun to penetrate this last unexplored region on earth, which holds the promise of new discoveries and a wealth of knowledge.

The deepest part of the ocean, Challenger Deep in the Marianas Trench (a deep ditch or furrow) off the island of Guam, is 36,198 feet straight down. That's seven miles below the surface of the Pacific Ocean! Mount Everest, the highest mountain in the world, could fit into the Challenger Deep and still be more than a *mile* from the surface.

This deepest part of the ocean is called the abyss. It is blacker than night all the time, since sunlight cannot penetrate water so deep. It is very cold—only a little above freezing—and the pressure is a crushing three and a half tons per square inch!

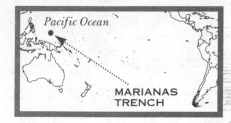

Do monstrous sea creatures of huge dimensions lurk in the abyss? Many scientists say no, but several believe they may indeed exist. Giant squids up to fifty-seven feet in length have already been found in the waters off New Zealand, and scientists believe there may be others that are even larger and more powerful. Giant squids of the Humboldt Current off Peru in South America are so ferocious and dangerous that they've been known to attack fishermen.

According to C. P. Idyll in his book *Abyss*, a type of eel larva six feet in length was discovered by a Danish research ship in the deep sea. "This suggests," wrote Idyll,

Do monstrous sea creatures lurk in the deepest part of the ocean?

"the existence of an enormous eel of sixty or seventy feet, a length that would surely qualify it as a sea monster."

Dr. Karl Shuker proposes the possibility of giant jellyfish whose stings are as deadly as those of the Australian sea wasp, another deadly denizen of the east Australian coast. "It is very possible that jellyfish notably larger than any yet recorded by science do exist in our world's vast oceans," declared Shuker. "Most may well exist in the abyssal depths, where man at present has scarcely begun to penetrate."

Only once has anyone ventured this deep. On January 23, 1960, Jacques Piccard and Lieutenant Donald Walsh of the United States Navy traveled to the bottom of the Marianas Trench in the bathyscaph *Trieste,* a specially designed diving apparatus.

The *Trieste* spent five hours descending into the Challenger Deep and only twenty minutes on the floor of the abyss. During that short time the men reported seeing nothing unusual.

The creatures that populate the ocean depths have adapted to the peculiar conditions in unusual ways. Most are quite bizarre in their appearance, yet small in their overall size. Gulpers are fish with huge mouths and small bodies. Hatchet fish also have large, gulping mouths and compressed bodies that are as thin as coins. Brotulids have big, grotesque heads that taper into long, pointed tails.

According to marine biologist Sylvia Earle, "It's still ironic that there are more footprints on the moon than there are on the bottom of the sea." Once the last great frontier of deep-ocean exploration is conquered, will scientists discover an abundance of new information to add to our knowledge of life on earth? Or will they encounter gigantic and threatening sea creatures and other monstrosities of nature? Only time will tell.

Hampton Court
Middlesex, England

Accompanied by two guards, the young woman with long, flowing hair suddenly broke loose from her captors and ran screaming through the gallery. Her husband, who was in the chapel hearing evening prayers, ignored his young wife's pleadings for mercy. The woman was recaptured and dragged away shrieking and sobbing by the guards, her screams strangely merging with the singing of the chapel choir.

The husband was King Henry VIII of England. The wife was Lady Catherine Howard, Henry's fifth spouse, who was eventually tried and found guilty of treason and beheaded in 1542. The incident occurred at Hampton Court, the beautiful palace by the River Thames where Henry often resided.

It's been more than 450 years since Lady Catherine's death. However, the tragic replay of her futile attempt to escape from King Henry's guards takes place nearly every year on or around the anniversary of the incident. Her ghost runs through what is now called "the Haunted Gallery" screaming and shrieking. Numerous witnesses have heard or seen her ghost.

MIDDLESEX, ENGLAND

Many other apparitions roam the grounds of Hampton Court including that of Henry's third wife, Jane Seymour. One of the few to keep her head, Jane Seymour died in 1537, only one week after bearing Henry his only son and heir, Prince Edward. Lady Jane's ghost, clad in white, wanders the halls carrying a lighted candle and often walks through doors and glides down staircases. Her ghost is responsible for many a servant handing in their resignation. Just imagine how unsettling it would be to see a specter of Lady Jane floating noiselessly toward you in a long, darkened corridor!

Then there's the story of the lady in gray, another ghostly resident. Princess Frederica of Hanover, a guest at Hampton Court, once came face to face with what she described as a "tall, gaunt figure dressed in a long gray robe, with a hood on her head and her lanky hands outstretched before her." Later the princess realized she had seen the ghost of Mrs. Sybil Penn, Prince Edward's nursemaid, who died there of smallpox in 1568.

In the nineteenth century a sealed room was discovered, which was believed to be Penn's. Her often-used spinning wheel was found inside. For years after the room was unsealed servants and guests at Hampton Court complained of cold hands on their faces, footsteps outside the door, loud crashing noises, strange lights, and voices at night.

Peter Underwood in *A Gazetteer of British Ghosts* relates an incident about two close female friends, one who was granted a residence at Hampton Court and the other who went to live in Germany. One night the Englishwoman saw a shadowy image of her friend, dressed entirely in black except for white gloves, climbing the staircase toward her. As the figure drew closer the Englishwoman fainted. Several days later the woman learned that her friend had died on the same day her ghost appeared at Hampton Court. Her friend had made an unusual request for her funeral. She wanted to be buried in black—with white gloves!

Hampton Court is rich in history with an underlying layer of violence and death. Only those with calm nerves should dare to visit this lively breeding ground of ghostly activities.

The Spy House Port Monmouth, New Jersey

The ghosts at the Spy House rattle appliances, make strange noises, push buttons, turn on radios, flip people's hair, move things around, and appear and disappear frequently. Some have even gone home with visitors they take a liking to.

This three-story wooden house, which was made into a museum in the late 1960s, is located on Sandy Hook Bay on the New Jersey coast. It is literally swarming with ghosts and other supernatural phenomena, whose frightening appearances have been witnessed often in broad daylight!

Arthur Myers in his book *A Ghosthunter's Guide* interviewed many people who experienced ghost sightings at the Spy House. One man described several children dressed in old-fashioned clothes playing near the house. "A girl ran through me," he said. "Then they were . . . gone."

A psychic named Gordon Banta recalled how he thought he had run over a little girl with his car, but when he left his vehicle to have a look around, he found no trace of her! The ghost suddenly appeared by his side and actually spoke to Banta. "She told me she lived in a house nearby . . . and had been run over by a horse and wagon."

The rich and varied history of the Spy House is thought to have contributed to the large number of spirits that are seen in and around the grounds. Barely a day goes by when a psychic does not visit the area to investigate.

The present building was put together from four smaller buildings that date back to the 1600s. One of these belonged to Thomas Whitlock, the first permanent white resident of New Jersey, who traded with the local Indians. Visions of brutal Indian attacks on the house were experienced by one visiting psychic who explained them as "energy imprints" from the past and not actual spirits.

During the Revolutionary War the house was used as an inn and tavern, often frequented by British Commander Lord Charles Cornwallis, whose ghost is often seen today. The inn was also used as a gathering place for American patriots who watched the movement of British ships in New York Harbor.

PORT MONMOUTH, NEW JERSEY

Pirates occupied the house in the early 1800s and are believed to have used it to hide stolen goods and even kill hostages. It is said that four tunnels exist behind the old stone walls in the cellar. Neidlinger believes the tunnels may still contain hidden pirate treasure and is trying to get a financial grant to explore this possibility.

Jane Dougherty of the Society of Parapsychology of New Jersey gets bad vibrations from the Spy House cellar. It was "used for many purposes, some of them involving fear and distress . . . " she said. "It was a place that pirates put people before they killed them. It was an animal slaughter room. It's a terrible feeling down there."

Author Myers explored the locked cellar with Neidlinger. He felt nothing unusual there, but his tape recorder behaved very strangely. It stopped then started again and later played back the sound of distorted voices. Myers assumed they were his and Neidlinger's voices, but he wasn't sure. Strangely enough the recorder worked fine once they were back upstairs.

Additional ghosts sighted in or around the Spy House include original owner Thomas Whitlock, a sea captain's wife named Abigail, Captain Morgan (the pirate) and his first mate, a childless woman named Penelope, a boy named Peter, and other children of assorted ages.

There's no question that strange things frequently happen at the Spy House, whose richly checkered past evidently lives on in the present.

America's Stonehenge Mystery Hill, North Salem, New Hampshire

This four-thousand-year-old stone complex of enclosed chambers, huge slabs, and narrow passageways may be the oldest man–made site in all of North America. Yet no one knows for sure who built it, where these people came from, and what purpose the complex served.

The mysterious stone structures of America's Stonehenge are surrounded by the rolling hills, green trees, and thick-growing shrubs of New England. It's easy to let your imagination wander as you walk up the trail past double stone walls to the first structure, known as the Watchhouse. Located outside the main complex, you wonder whether the guards of a mysterious prehistoric people once watched for unwelcome intruders from this vantage point.

From here a double-walled path leads to the main complex of stone structures. They're all about five feet high with roofs made of six- to ten-ton slabs of rock. How could such heavy stones (monoliths), which are held together by their own weight and careful positioning, have been raised up so high?

Next you come to a giant four-and-one-half-ton grooved slab known as the sacrificial table, which is supported on four stone legs. It's not hard to imagine people in dark hooded robes who may have surrounded this altar of sacrifice. Perhaps a human or animal victim was laid out before them on the slab amidst the sounds of strange chants and incantations, then a sharpened object was held high above the victim's chest and . . .

Turning away, you notice the grooves cut into the slab, which most researchers agree carried the runoff of blood underneath the rock to a network of stone drains.

Near the sacrificial table is a covered passage that leads to the largest structure in the complex, the Oracle Chamber. It's twenty-two-and-one-half feet wide and six- and-one-half feet high. A tubelike shaft leads from the large chamber directly under the sacrifical slab. Speaking through this opening, a person's voice in the large chamber is amplified and easily heard at the altar.

The outside area contains large stone monoliths arranged in a circular pattern. Robert Stone, owner of America's Stonehenge, found that many of these monoliths have astronomical significance. Standing at the sacrificial table, Stone discovered that the sun rose and set directly over certain monoliths. Two stones aligned with the setting sun at the annual summer and winter solstices on June 21 and December 21, respectively. Others marked sunrises and sunsets on important days of ancient pre-Christian holidays.

Just who were these prehistoric people who practiced human and/or animal sacrifice yet had an advanced knowledge of construction and astronomy? There are many theories.

Researcher Jean Hunt proposed a theory of a superior civilization that existed thousands of years ago but died out completely, leaving no records behind. Perhaps, according to Hunt, knowledge of this civilization came to us in the form of myths and legends that dealt with powerful magicians, wizards, or elves. Did such beings really once exist in the past, but are now only preserved in children's stories?

Scientists as well as psychics who have studied the site disagree on whether the people who built America's Stonehenge were native to North America or once came from ancient Europe. One theory states that a small group of people from prehistoric Europe migrated here so they could practice their beliefs of blood sacrifice freely and without persecution. Another theory holds that an ancient but highly intelligent race of people were wiped out in some type of massive disaster that destroyed their civilization, leaving behind only the ruins in New Hampshire.

America's Stonehenge is a scary and mysterious place that is totally enveloped by the past. Standing among the stone chambers and monoliths, it's easy to understand how certain psychic or sensitive individuals could pick up strong vibrations from a previous era. Perhaps someday the puzzle will be solved. In the meantime the research and study continue and the mystery remains.

Just who built the mysterious stone structures known as America's Stonehenge?

Glamis Castle
Glamis, Angus, Scotland

I t doesn't matter whether you visit Glamis Castle on a dark and stormy night or in the bright sunlight of a summer's day. You can't help but feel that this impressive and huge structure is a very scary, strange, and mysterious place.

Built in the fourteenth century, Glamis is the oldest inhabited castle in Scotland and is home to frequently sighted ghosts and spirits. The castle was originally the residence of the lords of Glamis, who lost their family fortune, after which the castle passed into the hands of Patrick Lyons in the mid-seventeenth century. Lyons renovated the place, built up the fortune, and was made the Earl of Strathmore.

ANGUS, SCOTLAND

According to legend, in the early nineteenth century the first son of the eleventh Earl of Strathmore was born terribly deformed. The child had a large, hairy egg-shaped body with no neck and tiny arms and legs. A special hidden room was built for him in the depths of the castle, and his existence was kept secret because of his horrible appearance.

The Monster of Glamis, as he came to be known, was the true heir to the castle and all the wealth that went with it. Only the Earl of Strathmore, his oldest normal son, the family lawyer, and the manager of the estate knew about him.

The monster was not expected to survive for very long, but he was very strong and outlived several generations of Strathmores. Each oldest son was told the awful secret when he reached the age of twenty-one.

It is said that the Strathmores were very unhappy, moody, and withdrawn men because of the secret existence of their monstrous relative. It wasn't until the early twentieth century that the creature was said to have died. It is believed that his corpse is bricked up somewhere within the walls of the castle.

No one knows where the secret room is located. Once, according to Peter Underwood in his book *A Gazetteer of British Ghosts,* a group of young people visited every one of the more than one hundred rooms in Glamis Castle and hung sheets out the windows to mark them. "They were sure that they had visited every room," wrote Underwood. "But when they gathered outside they counted seven windows in the massive castle with nothing hanging from them." The mystery as to why more windows are seen from the outside than the inside remains unexplained.

The ghost of an unidentified small woman is a frequent sight in the castle chapel, even in broad daylight. The sunlight coming through the windows has been seen shining directly through the woman's figure.

Another female figure frequently appears above the clock tower, enveloped by a reddish glow. She is thought to be Janet Douglas, the wife of the sixth Lord of Glamis, who was suspected of poisoning her husband. In 1537 she was accused of trying to poison King James V and was burned at the stake.

Unusual and frightening noises are often heard within the castle walls, including stamping and swearing from the tower and hammering and loud knocking sounds. There's even a door that opens by itself every night, no matter how well locked or secured it is.

There are more than enough spirits and supernatural phenomena at Glamis Castle to impress even the most skeptical ghost watcher.

West Bengal, India

The young man had planned a surprise visit to friends and relatives in a distant village. As was the custom among those who were poor and lived in India, he began his travels after dark in order to escape the extreme heat of the day. He was prepared to walk through the night and hoped to reach his destination, a twenty-mile journey, by early morning. He traveled light, carrying only some food and water, and like most Indians of his class, his legs and feet were bare.

The road was no wider than a trail and the surface was covered by several inches of dust. Walking at a fairly brisk pace, the young man's bare foot came down directly on the coiled back of an Indian cobra snake (called the common cobra), which was lying quite comfortably and somewhat hidden from view in the warm road.

The snake reacted so quickly to what it believed to be an attack that the young man had no time to respond. The six-foot-long cobra spread its frightening hood, arched its neck, and struck at the young man's legs with a sharp hissing sound.

Biting the youth's foot, it held on with its short fangs and injected a large amount of its powerful venom into the flesh. The young man screamed and tried to kick the snake away, but he knew immediately that he was doomed. In such an isolated spot there was no way to find an antivenin in time to save his life.

He screamed for help, but no one heard his cries. Within fifteen minutes of the bite, the young man's eyelids began to droop. He had difficulty swallowing and felt weak and confused. Gasping for air, his pulse became irregular. The poisonous venom was rapidly taking its toll on his nervous system and weakening his heart and lungs. Soon his system shut down completely and the young man quietly passed away, one of the fifteen thousand people who die each year in India of snakebites.

Certain districts in the Indian state of West Bengal in the Ganges River Delta report an annual death rate twice as high as the entire country—about eleven deaths from snakebites per one hundred thousand population. This is a frighteningly high statistic, and it may be even higher since so many villages are so isolated that they may not report incidents of snakebites.

India is a country of nearly nine hundred million people, more than three times larger than the population of the United States and crowded into an area one-third its size. This density of population coupled with the large number of dangerous Asiatic snakes in the region results in this astonishingly high death rate from snakebites.

Certain districts in West Bengal report an annual death rate from snakebites twice as high as the entire country of India.

Several other factors contribute to the problem as well. Most Indians seldom wear shoes or leggings to protect their feet and legs, and many travel at night when their chances of accidentally confronting a deadly snake are greater, since several lethal varieties are nocturnal species. In addition, snakes and other creatures are protected and not killed in India because many of the people believe in reincarnation, namely that the soul and spirit of a person can be reborn into an animal.

Housing construction among the masses is generally of poor quality, and many Indians sleep on the floor. Snakes that prowl at night are attracted to villages by the prevalence of mice and rats, which are their favorite foods. During the rainy season snakes gravitate to high ground along with people and enter homes and even beds. Sleepers are often bitten by kraits, a type of snake that is more common in populated areas and whose venom is similar to the cobra.

India is also home to the king cobra, the largest, most poisonous snake in the world. The king cobra averages eight to twelve feet in length, with the biggest on record measuring eighteen feet four inches. Imagine a snake that large and dangerous and ready to strike!

There are many unique and wondrous attractions that draw visitors to India from throughout the world, including the Taj Mahal, one of the most beautiful buildings on earth. If you're planning an Indian vacation soon, be sure to choose a pair of sturdy knee-high hiking boots. And it wouldn't hurt to bring along a snakebite kit. *Bon Voyage!*

Cheesman Park Denver, Colorado

At first glance Cheesman Park appears to be a beautiful and pleasant place, a touch of green in the middle of a busy city. The lawns are carefully maintained and the dignified old trees provide shady spots for visitors.

Kids play here. People relax, take walks, engage in conversation, or sit and feed the squirrels and birds. Except for the Cheesman Memorial Pavilion, which is made of white marble and was built to resemble the Greek Parthenon, Cheesman Park is not much different from thousands of other parks in thousands of other American cities.

Or is it?

For beneath the well-manicured lawns and stately trees and gardens, right under the feet of the happy children and chattering adults, are the abandoned graves and forgotten bodies of dozens of Denver citizens. And you can be sure these spirits are not resting in peace! When their story is told it's not surprising that people say Cheesman Park is haunted and that ghostly apparitions are frequently reported in and around the area.

In 1858 one of Denver's founders, William Larimer, set aside this land for a town cemetery. It was first called Mount Prospect, but eventually the name was changed to City Cemetery.

By the 1880s ownership of the cemetery had passed from William Larimer to his assistant John J. Walley. By this time it was run down, badly maintained, and an embarrassing eyesore for the city. In 1890 the U.S. government assumed ownership of the land when it was discovered that it was part of an old Indian treaty. They, in turn, sold it to the city of Denver, which made plans to turn the area into a park.

City officials announced that friends and families had ninety days to relocate the bodies of their loved ones from City Cemetery. Unfortunately, five thousand of the dead remained unclaimed. These bodies were removed in 1893 by an undertaker named McGovern. The city contracted for each body to be dug up and placed in a new three-and-one-half-foot box for reburial in Denver's Riverside Cemetery.

As time passed, the workmen got progressively careless. Instead of carefully prying open the caskets, they smashed them open with shovels. Bodies that hadn't decayed enough to fit into the small coffins were broken into pieces. Body parts often were mixed up and placed in the wrong caskets.

No prayers were said for the dead, no respect given to the poor souls whose bodies were thoughtlessly shoveled into the boxes. It was around this time that residents in the area reported seeing apparitions and hearing sorrowful cries and moaning coming from the cemetery at night.

Soon the newspapers began covering the bizarre and horrible activities at the cemetery. When it was discovered that questionable financial transactions were taking place, a big scandal erupted. The project was immediately

DENVER,
COLORADO

stopped and an investigation begun. The rest of the bodies were left in the cemetery. Soon they were abandoned and forgotten. Landscaping for the park began years later, and in 1907 the portion that covered City Cemetery was named after a prominent citizen of Denver, Walter Cheesman.

Some park visitors have detected a sad and disturbing undercurrent of feelings intertwined with the pleasant, happy surroundings. Perhaps it's the mournful spirits of the forsaken dead. Do they continue to search in vain for a proper burial ground where they can finally rest in peace?

The courageous person who walks down shadowy pathways of the park at night may see some interesting apparitions in the moonlight . . . if he or she doesn't run away, screaming, too quickly!

Amazon River, Brazil

"On September 19, 1981, more than 300 people were reportedly killed and eaten when an overloaded passenger-cargo boat capsized and sank as it was docking at the Brazilian port of Obidos. According to one official, only 178 of the boat's passengers survived."

—*Guinness Book of Records 1994*

The creatures responsible for this horrible incident were piranhas, the most ferocious freshwater fish in the world. Only two species of piranhas can inflict such terrible damage on people—the red-bellied piranhas and the black piranhas. Both types inhabit the slow-moving waters of the Amazon River in Brazil, South America.

The Amazon River is 3,900 miles long and flows through numerous freshwater channels in northern Brazil before finally draining into the Atlantic Ocean. The heavy rainfall and hot, humid weather conditions in the Amazon create an ideal environment for piranhas. During the rainy season these frightening fish thrive in the river's flood-plain, which measures nearly thirty miles across.

Piranhas grow up to fourteen inches in length and are noted for their sharp teeth and powerful jaws. The triangular-shaped upper and lower teeth slide against each other to bite off chunks of flesh, which are then swallowed whole.

Piranhas eat other fish as well as fruits, seeds, and even plants. They especially enjoy the flesh of dead animals and people. In fact, some rainforest people use the piranha's lethal efficiency to dispose of their dead when the river floods its banks during the rainy season. Since bodies can't be buried when there is flooding, they are left in the river. Within hours the piranhas eat all the corpses' flesh so that only the skeletons are left. The bones are then recovered, dried, and eventually buried.

AMAZON RIVER, BRAZIL

Piranhas are so thorough in eating flesh off a skeleton that it's often difficult to determine the cause of death. In the ferryboat accident noted by the *Guinness Book of Records,* the proficiency of these deadly fish made it nearly impossible to determine the cause of death of the victims. Some may have been attacked by schools of piranhas while flailing around in the water just after the boat capsized. Others may have drowned first and then had their bodies eaten by the vicious fish.

Regardless of what may have happened, South Americans who live along the banks of the Amazon have learned to carefully coexist and even avail themselves of these frightening creatures. The flesh of piranhas is used as food, their jaws as cutting tools, and their teeth as razors. Though some may say piranhas are more useful dead than alive, they do contribute to the environment in several ways. Piranhas eat dead flesh in the river that might otherwise poison the water, and they control the fish population by eating diseased and weaker ones.

Brazil may have more than its share of beautiful sandy beaches and vacation spots, but thanks to the pesky piranhas, the Amazon River frightens away as many tourists as it attracts.

With its densely forested, lush green surroundings, the Amazon River may appear deliciously enticing, tempting you to soak those aching arches after a long day of sightseeing in the rain forest. But remember, if you dangle your feet here, you may come up a few toes shy!

Pirhanas grow up to fourteen inches in length and are noted for their razor-sharp teeth and powerful jaws.

114

Interstate 65 Between Evergreen and Greenville, Alabama

It looks like a perfectly normal stretch of road, like so many others throughout the state of Alabama.

In official reports the police refer to it as "open country." Others say it's a lonely and isolated stretch through forested land. A few go so far as to describe it as "spooky" and "haunted."

One thing is definite, though. Something strange and scary is happening on Interstate 65 between the small towns of Evergreen and Greenville, and even the police can't explain it! The facts clearly show that the number of accidents on this forty-mile stretch of I-65 is considerably higher than average. And the big mystery is why?

Judge for yourself: In the time period from 1987 through mid-October of 1994, there have been 724 accidents recorded. According to statistics supplied by Waymon Benifield of the Alabama Department of Transportation in Montgomery, 989 vehicles were involved in these accidents, nearly 400 people were injured, and 31 were killed.

Some say it's just a coincidence. County Sheriff Edwin Booker once declared that "drivers simply lose interest." Were they so hypnotized by the straight and flat terrain that they lost their concentration, as the police seem to think? But the country is full of straight, flat roads whose accident statistics are nowhere near the high figures of Interstate 65 between Evergreen and Greenville, Alabama!

There's talk in the area that this portion of the highway was constructed over sacred Creek Indian burial grounds. Many locals believe that the spirits of the Indians, whose graves were disturbed, are exerting some kind of power over the drivers.

Are drivers swerving to avoid visions of ghosts or other apparitions that appear out of nowhere on the highway? Are angry spirits causing drivers to lapse into a trancelike state and lose control of their cars?

Tribal Chairman Eddie Tullis of the local Creek Indian reservation stated, "A lot of our people's graves were disturbed by the interstate," but he stopped short of blaming Indian spirits for the accidents. "I think if people consider how the Indians have been mistreated," said Tullis in *More Haunted Houses* by Joan Bingham and Delores Riccio, "it could cause them to lose their attention while on the road."

INTERSTATE 65, ALABAMA

One might expect an increase in accidents in the winter months at night when the weather was bad and visibility limited. Yet the data clearly shows that over 60 percent of the accidents took place in the daylight hours, when it was clear or cloudy and the roads were dry, not wet, icy, or snowy.

Surprisingly most accidents occurred in the summer months on straight level stretches where the driver's vision was not obstructed in any way. Most drivers were wide awake, alert, and paying attention.

It's even more mysterious when you consider that the majority of the accidents involved only one vehicle!

Has a large amount of hostile energy built up in this area? Apparently so. In addition to having their sacred burial grounds disturbed, the Creek Indians were forced by the Federal government in the 1830s to leave their homes in Alabama and resettle on reservations in Oklahoma. According to Bingham and Riccio, thousands died in the migration west.

No one really knows what's causing the high number of accidents on that portion of the Interstate in southern Alabama. But one thing is certain. If you find yourself driving there one day, keep awake, stay alert, and be very, very careful—no matter how beautiful the day may seem!

Mammoth and Crystal Caves, Mammoth Cave National Park, Kentucky

J oy Lyons, a guide at Mammoth Cave, had just led a group of tourists along with two other park rangers to a place in the big cave called the Church. Here the guides turned off the lights so the tourists could "have a sensory experience."

Suddenly Lyons was shoved hard on the right shoulder so forcefully that she almost toppled over. At that exact instant one of the rangers lit a lantern and Lyons saw, to her amazement, that no one else in the cave was even remotely close to where she was standing.

Who pushed her? Was it one of the several ghosts and apparitions that have appeared out of nowhere to dozens of visitors and guides, only to disappear just as fast? Or was it just Lyons' imagination playing tricks on her?

MAMMOTH CAVE, KENTUCKY

Arthur Myers in his book *A Ghosthunter's Guide* interviewed numerous people who have experienced strange and unexplained phenomena in both Mammoth Cave and Crystal Cave (two attractions in Mammoth Cave National Park), and Joy Lyons was just one of them.

Even without the possibility of ghosts, Mammoth Cave's underground caverns and passageways are frightening enough. It's certainly a place where one would rather not be left alone. Becky Dahle, a supervisor of the attraction's guides, told Myers, "If there ever was a place under the earth where people's imaginations could play tricks on them, it's Mammoth Cave. It's a deprivational thing," she explained. "There's no natural light, no natural sound." In other words, it's pretty creepy.

Mammoth Cave is the largest cave in the world, estimated to be about 340 million years old. It's easy to get hopelessly lost here, since there are 330 miles of passageways on five different levels. A mummified body of an Indian man, more than two thousand years old, has been found here along with other evidence of early human habitation.

Many guides and tourists have had strange experiences. One believed he saw the ghost of a famous guide from the nineteenth century named Stephen Bishop, a former slave who always wore a large Panama hat. Several have seen a man in old-fashioned dress standing apart from the main group of tourists.

Crystal Cave, located five miles from Mammoth Cave, is known for the bizarre death of its one-time owner, Floyd Collins, in 1925. He became trapped under a rock overhang and for sixteen days rescue attempts to free Collins were reported in newspapers throughout the country. He died after an unexpected cave-in, and his glass-topped coffin was displayed in the cave as a tourist attraction for a number of years.

Many strange occurrences at Crystal Cave have been linked to the ghost of Floyd Collins. One employee distinctly heard a man's voice faintly crying, "Help! Help me, Johnny, I'm trapped!" It's interesting to note that the last person to talk with Floyd Collins before the cave-in was his friend Johnny Gerald!

People's voices in conversation, candles flaming up for no apparent reason, sounds of rhythmic banging, flapping noises like the wings of birds, an ancient crank-up telephone that's disconnected but suddenly rings—all of these were experienced at Crystal Cave by a variety of people.

Are there ghosts in Mammoth Cave and Crystal Cave?

According to author Myers, "If there aren't, a lot of people are hallucinating."

Suicide Pool
Epping Forest, England

Early one morning in the summer of 1914 a man was taking a walk on one of the many hiking trails in Epping Forest, ten miles northeast of the city of London. As he neared a body of water popularly known as the Suicide Pool, he noticed the figure of a man lying facedown in a ditch. Another man, overweight and stocky, was standing over the apparently dead body with a gun still clutched in his hand.

Impulsively the man approached the armed man to question him. Before he could get a single word out of his mouth, however, both the man with the gun and the body in the ditch disappeared right before his eyes.

Did the man imagine the bizarre scene? No one knows for sure.

Two days later the body of a former soldier was found lying facedown in the same ditch. The poor man had clearly died from gunshot wounds, and the police listed his death as a homicide. The murderer was never caught, and the man's death remains one of the many strange mysteries that surround the Suicide Pool and its vicinity in Epping Forest.

According to Elliott O'Donnell in his book *The Great Ghost Hunter,* "There is no pool of water in England which has been the scene of more suicides and murders and . . . which is more sinister in reputation . . . "

One of Europe's oldest forests, Epping is a six-thousand-acre maze of hiking paths and horsetrails crisscrossed by roadways. Legislation passed in 1878 established a portion of the forest to be preserved for recreational activities. Formally opened to the public by Queen Victoria in 1882,

Epping Forest is located near the towns of Woodford and Waltham and is easily accessible to Londoners by railway.

Surrounded by trees, the Suicide Pool is a dark and still body of water. A number of murders have been associated with the area but one of the better-known cases is the unsolved mystery of a pretty young servant named Emma Morgan. She was last seen alive walking toward Epping Forest with a baby in her arms. Morgan's husband had thrown her and her child out of the house when he discovered the baby wasn't his.

On that particular day Emma Morgan and her child were not only homeless, but penniless as well. It's possible she may have been heading to the Suicide Pool to end her misery, but the woman never made it. The bodies of Morgan and her baby were found brutally murdered next to the water. The killer was never found.

Author O'Donnell visited the Suicide Pool one moonlit autumn night and had several frightening experiences. Although totally alone, he distinctly heard someone cough, the faint cry of a child in pain, and then the sounds of a group of people steadily marching toward the pool. When the tramping sounds stopped, O'Donnell clearly saw several black-robed figures holding a coffin. Hearing a noise from the opposite direction, he turned and saw an image of an "evil-looking" young man bending over the body of a woman. According to O'Donnell, "Picking up the body, he came staggering with it to the pool and threw the body into the still, gleaming water." Then the images faded and all was quiet again.

O'Donnell described his strange experience to an older man who had lived near Epping Forest for many years. The man brought out old newspaper clippings that described the unsolved case of a woman who had been murdered and thrown into the Suicide Pool in 1887.

Is the area around the Suicide Pool so imprinted with tragedy and bloodshed that certain sensitive individuals experience violent replays of the past and terrible visions of the future?

O'Donnell thought so. What do you think?

Alcatraz
San Francisco, California

Walking down the now-vacant corridors of what once was the U. S. Penitentiary at Alcatraz, one finds the cell doors propped open, one after the other, leading into empty, stark cubicles. A strange and eerie timelessness hovers in the air here, as if the past were permanently imprisoned within the same walls where so many convicts were once locked behind bars.

What's that? A clang of metal doors, the sound of men's voices? Turning around quickly, you see there is nothing there—only emptiness. Yet some security guards and tour guides have reported hearing similar sounds here—screaming, whistling, even the sound of feet running along the corridors.

For nearly thirty years the U. S. Penitentiary at Alcatraz was a place of violence, brutality, and loneliness. Now a national park and popular tourist attraction, it is not at all surprising that this once harsh and dismal place is said to be haunted by the frightening sounds of the past.

First used as a fortress to protect San Francisco Bay during Civil War days, the rocky island became a military prison in 1861. By the 1920s stories circulated concerning the severity of life at Alcatraz. One San Francisco newspaper reporter called it "Uncle Sam's Devil's Island,"

comparing it to the famous penal colony of Devil's Island off French Guiana in the Caribbean Sea.

In 1933 the Department of Justice acquired the island, and on July 1, 1934, Alcatraz became a U.S. penitentiary. It was converted to a maximum security prison in response to the nationwide crime wave of the 1930s. Only dangerous, difficult, and desperate inmates were sent here to serve "hard time." They were murderers, rapists, and gangsters and included the likes of Al Capone and Machine Gun Kelly.

Surrounded by San Francisco Bay, "the rock" seemed virtually impossible to escape from. Yet there were eight escape attempts from Alcatraz. Five were stopped by bullets, and the others were presumed drowned in the frigid waters of the Bay. On May 2, 1946, six inmates attempted to break out by capturing several guards. In the gun battle that followed, three of the inmates and two of the guards were killed and several others were wounded.

Surrounded by San Francisco Bay, "the rock" was virtually impossible to escape from.

The most famous break occurred on June 11, 1962, when Frank Lee Morris, Clarence Anglin, and John Anglin chipped out a tunnel through concrete and then used the prison ventilation system to escape from the cellhouse. They made their way to the water and were never heard from again. To this day it's uncertain whether the men drowned or actually escaped to the mainland.

According to Rosemary Ellen Guiley in *The Encyclopedia of Ghosts and Spirits,* "Insanity was the kindest fate to befall a prisoner—others committed suicide, murdered one another, or died unpleasant deaths from illness and disease. Beatings by guards were routine," wrote Guiley, "and the screams of the beaten reverberated throughout the cells."

The worst conditions at Alcatraz were found in solitary confinement cells in Block D (called "holes" by the inmates) where many men either became very ill, went insane, or died. A prisoner was stripped naked, beaten, and kept in complete darkness in a tiny cement cell with only a hole in the floor for a bathroom. Bread and water were fed to the prisoners twice a day and every third day they were given a full meal.

Do the sounds of a violent past replay themselves over and over again in the empty corridors of Alcatraz? Are these sounds just the result of an overactive imagination stimulated by such a strange and scary setting? Perhaps. But some believe that the death, savagery, and horror that took place within the prison walls can never be completely erased.

Bachelor's Grove Cemetery, Rubio Woods Chicago, Illinois

The dead don't rest easy at Bachelor's Grove Cemetery! How else could you explain the reports of strange lights, unusual cold, ghostly apparitions, phantom cars, and spirit voices?

It's no wonder that this cemetery is considered by many to be one of the most haunted in the world. Dale Kaczmarek, head of the Ghost Research Society, has documented the scary and mysterious phenomena that have occurred here over the years.

Consider the following:

CHICAGO, ILLINOIS

- One woman reported colliding with a car at a nearby intersection. When she got out to inspect her front fender, the other car had disappeared and there was absolutely no damage to her vehicle.
- There have been numerous reports of a phantom red skyrocket zooming above the main path leading to the cemetery, leaving a red trail behind it. And some of these lights, according to Kaczmarek, "have been seen in broad daylight"!
- Many visitors to the cemetery have seen the apparitions of a woman carrying a baby, a dark-hooded figure, and a mysterious black carriage.

In addition, a number of people have observed a phantom farmhouse that appears and then vanishes without a trace. Whether it's in daylight or evening, "the description of the house," explained Kaczmarek, "remains constant: a white farmhouse with white wooden pillars, a porch swing, and a light burning faintly in the window."

He continued, "As the house is approached by witnesses, it begins to shrink and get smaller and smaller until the image itself disappears from sight. No one has ever made it to the front steps. . . . " he added. Could the farmhouse be the entrance to another dimension?

German immigrants originally settled in the area in the 1830s, which was given its name because of the large number of unmarried men living there. One acre of land was set aside for the graveyard, and burials continued there until 1965. The cemetery is surrounded by an eight-foot-high fence riddled by holes. The main gates are broken and everything is overgrown with weeds and other foliage.

Inside, the gravestones have been vandalized, moved, and marked with graffiti and spray paint. According to Kaczmarek, during the 1920s and 1930s gangsters used the lagoon to dump dead bodies. In l964 and 1975 some graves were dug up and caskets broken into. In the middle 1970s rangers found evidence of voodoo and devil worship. Could the dark-hooded figure have some connection to this black magic?

It's interesting to note that within the fence bordering the cemetery there are no squirrels, birds, chipmunks, or other animals. "It is literally devoid of life," explained Kaczmarek. Yet, just outside the fence, plenty of these animals can been seen and heard in the Rubio Woods. Do the animals sense that all is not right at Bachelor's Grove? Are the troubled spirits unhappy because their final resting places have been disturbed and violated? No one knows.

The animals have decided to stay away. But many curious people still continue to find the courage to investigate this scary and haunted place.

Will you be one of them?

Index